Garden BirdWatch Handbook

Contents

Garden birds are not only beautiful and fascinating but of great interest to science. Some are also declining, causing serious conservation concern. More scientific papers have probably been published about Great Tits than any other species of wild bird.

*by **Andrew Cannon.***
ISBN 0 903793 98 9

Published in 1998 by and available from:
British Trust for Ornithology
The Nunnery, Thetford,
IP24 2PU
Telephone 01842 750050

If you have access to a garden, can recognise the common birds that visit it and are not already a Garden BirdWatch participant we would very much welcome your help. Please contact the BTO for details.

Text and figures copyright © British Trust for Ornithology 1998. The BTO must be fully acknowledged in any quotation. Illustrations © and used by kind permission of: *Tom Holden (fc,1,35,54,67) (© BTO, 48,62,63,64,68,70,71,72) Simon Gillings (3) Natural History Museum, London (4) Andrew Cannon (5,6,9,18,19,24,25,46,58,66,74,75,77) Ray Waters (7) CJ Wildbird Foods (10,11,31) Humphrey Crick (14,15,23,56,60,79) Andy Wilson (16) Su Gough (18) Susan Paterson (21) Mike Weston (© BTO, 22,57) Ray Marsh (26) Colin Varndell (© BTO, 27,40,49,53) Roger Tidman (28,36,37,38,39,41,42,51,55,bc) Keith Bailey (33) Derek Toomer (43,47,50,65) Eric & David Hosking (45) Jill Burry (44) Jacky Prior (59)*

Special thanks to: Roger Tidman, Wildlife Photographer, 01263 860776

Chris Whittles, CJ Wildbird Foods, 01743 709545

Front cover picture: Blue Tit (adult in winter) by Tom Holden.
Back cover picture: Blue Tit (juvenile in summer) by Roger Tidman

Printing of this handbook was funded by a grant from the Committee on the Public Understanding of Science. The BTO/CJ Garden BirdWatch is funded by participants' contributions and supported by CJ Wildbird Foods Ltd.

PROMOTING SCIENCE
ENGINEERING & TECHNOLOGY

Andrew would like to thank:
Graham Appleton, Nigel Clark, Humphrey Crick, Martin George, David Glue, Jeremy Greenwood, Tom Holden, David Hosking, Jen Keddy John Lawton, Sue Lincoln, Chris Mead, Ian Newton, Jacky Prior, Robert Prŷs-Jones, Derek Toomer and all Garden BirdWatch participants.

Opinions expressed are not necessarily those of the BTO, its Council or committees. The author is solely responsible for any errors.
Colour origination by Swaingrove Reprographics, Bury St Edmunds, IP30 9ND. Printed by Reflex Litho, Thetford, IP24 1HG.

Acknowledgements

If you keep regular records of your bird observations, however simple, you are already an ornithologist. The longer you keep records, the more rewarding they become. Wouldn't it be even more interesting if everyone recorded birds in the same way, so their data could be easily combined? And how productive these records could be if we all subscribed a little money towards employing scientists, to analyse them and publish the results! That was exactly the thinking behind the creation of the British Trust for Ornithology in 1933. Thousands of enthusiasts who really care about birds are collecting the data which enable both campaigners and decision-makers to establish (and hopefully agree!) conservation priorities.

Studying the anatomy and evolution of birds are important parts of ornithology but need trained researchers and costly equipment. The BTO concentrates on the numbers, movements and survival of wild birds as these can be effectively monitored by amateur volunteers. As we gather more records from different habitats we learn more about the resources birds need. With this ecological information we are also researching and promoting good habitat management for bird conservation.

Even with many volunteers, we can't monitor every wild bird in the British Isles. BTO scientists design surveys which record samples of the birds in examples of various habitats, including gardens. Using statistical tests, we determine how accurately these samples really represent the whole population. For these tests to work, the data has to be gathered in ways which can sometimes seem a little odd, but it is this careful survey design and analysis that makes our work 'scientific' and gives it the credibility to influence conservation and bird protection decisions.

Studying familiar birds and learning more about their numbers and movements is just as interesting as 'ticking' new species although sometimes slightly different in approach. Negative records are vital, especially if birds were expected. In an ornithologist's notebook, "no birds seen" written in a garden where sparrows used to feed may be more relevant to conservation than notes on a rare vagrant. Mind you, many top 'twitchers' are also BTO volunteers, all of us united by caring about birds and their future, in a unique partnership of amateurs and professionals.

This booklet is dedicated to the Garden BirdWatch volunteers all over the British Isles who are contributing to scientific ornithology with such great enthusiasm. It aims to share that enthusiasm and to illustrate the importance and fascination of studying well-known birds. It is not primarily an identification aid although hints and tips for each species are given, along with the latest population estimates for the British Isles (numbers of breeding pairs unless otherwise stated), conservation status summaries and plots of the first three years' Garden BirdWatch weekly reporting rates. These are simply the percentage of our participants observing that species in their gardens. We also try to highlight some of the valuable contributions to our knowledge of birds and their conservation which have come from studying 'common or garden' species.

" Bird watching is either the most scientific of sports or the most sporting of sciences."   E.M.Nicholson, *The Art of Bird Watching*, 1931.

The importance of monitoring bird populations.

Are some familiar wild birds decreasing in numbers? Are others becoming more common? Interesting questions, but why are they important? Monitoring endangered species is obviously vital but even well-known birds cannot be taken for granted. The High BTO Alert issued for the House Sparrow shows that monitoring 'common or garden' species may uncover surprising problems. Passenger Pigeons and Great Auks were hunted from abundance to extinction. Modern laws and conservation awareness make such deliberate destruction less likely today but nonetheless many birds are still declining alarmingly, indirectly affected by human activities causing loss or deterioration of their habitats. So bird populations are not just worth monitoring for their own sake, but also for what they tell us about the environment. Changes in their numbers reflect the condition of the countryside in which they have to survive. Most people agree that we should aim to hand the planet Earth on to our children more or less intact. To balance development with preserving the environment we need cost-effective and practical methods of monitoring the condition of the natural world. Birds are relatively easy to see and identifying them is a popular hobby so reliable records can be provided by volunteers.

In the early 1960s many birds were badly affected by pesticides. The eggs of birds of prey were damaged by poisons accumulating in their food chain. Such a 'bottleneck' at a particular stage of a bird's life cycle can cause a rapid population decline. The worst pesticides were banned and birds of prey have more or less recovered. Because bird populations can respond so quickly, they are sensitive and useful indicators of the health of our environment. If the poisons were affecting birds so badly, it is likely they would have compromised our own health eventually. On the principle of the 'Canary in the Coal Mine', by monitoring birds we can quickly detect changes in the environment that we have to share with them.

Passenger Pigeons were incredibly abundant in America but had been hunted to extinction by 1914. Habitat destruction made them more vulnerable.

For a bird population to remain stable, enough individuals must overcome a series of seasonal challenges the toughest of which are reproducing and surviving the winter. How successfully the birds negotiate these hurdles each year largely determines their numbers and this is greatly affected by human activities as well as natural factors. But analysing the causes of breeding or wintering problems is not straightforward. Each stage of a bird's life cycle may be affected by different problems, including predation, nest sites, weather, food, roosting sites, competition and natural change of the habitat. And the timing of a problem may not be obvious as birds often need to prepare for difficult times in advance. Low winter survival of Skylarks might actually be due to the disappearance of autumn stubbles, leaving them in poor condition as winter approaches. Reduced breeding success in Yellowhammers might actually be due to food shortages earlier in spring weakening the adults. So the BTO tries to monitor birds at all stages of their lives and in different kinds of habitat, by integrating data from different surveys.

As well as dramatically affecting birds at particular stages of their life cycles, our activities may cause subtle problems that we might not detect if we just compared two successive years' bird counts. Creeping suburbia, developments in farming, climate change and even fashions in gardening or pets may slowly affect our bird populations. The introduction of an alien species or the loss

These Tree Sparrows have already survived from egg to hatchling and from hatchling to fledgling, two major life cycle challenges. How many will survive to breed next year?

of a habitat can have surprising 'knock-on' effects long after the initial events are forgotten. It's vital to monitor long-term trends to spot such insidious problems. Populations of small birds such as Wrens vary widely from year to year for entirely natural reasons. If we only collected a few years' data we might be misled into inappropriate conservation policies by a short term crash or boom when the underlying trend might be quite different. So as well as monitoring birds at different stages of their life cycle, we need to monitor them over a range of time scales. As more data are collected over longer periods the BTO can use more accurate analytical methods. 'BTO Alerts' are now issued whenever our volunteers' data causes concern.

BTO survey projects reflect the range of interests and skills among bird enthusiasts, enabling anyone to contribute to an integrated bird population monitoring programme. The BTO/JNCC/RSPB Breeding Bird Survey requires the experience and commitment to identify every bird seen and heard on regular visits to a site whose exact location is chosen randomly by a computer. Over 2,000 dedicated birders contribute to this project which is carefully designed to produce data appropriate for the latest computer analysis techniques and will provide our best estimates of breeding bird populations. Sites may turn out to be some distance from home and can at first seem rather uninteresting but once you keep regular records, it's amazing how fascinating the most unpromising site can become.

The annual Heronries Census, Europe's longest-running bird survey, is simple but monitors the environment well because Herons are predators, at the top of a complex food web. Most of their prey live in water, an ecosystem particularly sensitive to factors such as pollution or climate. Adult Herons are hard to count as they are very mobile but volunteers estimate the breeding population by counting their nests, which even beginners can locate. Other BTO single species projects include Skylark, Lapwing, Rook and Nightingale surveys.

Garden BirdWatch is a habitat project recording relative numbers of birds using gardens at different times of year. Declines or increases can be spotted and compared with the situation in other habitats. It is particularly interesting to study birds in gardens at this time of great change in our countryside. Gardens have become progressively more important for birds in the last few years and in some areas may well offer them more resources than the surrounding farms or woods. So changes in the birds visiting gardens may be linked to issues of great conservation and economic significance such as farming subsidies or forestry policies. Other BTO habitat projects survey birds of wetlands, waterways, woodlands and farmland.

Life history projects identify the particular stages in their life cycles at which wild birds are experiencing difficulties and so enable scarce conservation resources to be effectively targetted. Over a million nest record cards carefully collected by BTO volunteers are an invaluable resource for investigating why a species is declining. It may be the numbers of eggs laid, eggs hatching or nestlings fledging that are changing, different problems which may well have completely different causes.

A volunteer carefully fits the correct size of ring to a Blackbird, recording age, sex and condition.

Volunteer bird ringers also provide important life history data by fitting birds with uniquely numbered rings and carefully recording if the same birds are subsequently caught again. Together with the rings from dead birds found and returned to the BTO by members of the public, this tells us how long birds are surviving. Nest records can be carefully collected by anyone, following a tried and tested BTO 'code of conduct', but ringing requires a special licence and training.

In the British Isles just a few tiny fragments of genuinely natural wildlife habitat remain. Caledonian pine forests and the bogs so threatened by garden peat extraction are internationally important ancient ecosystems but some significant habitats, such as heaths and broads, were created by human activity and have only subsequently developed their unique and precious wildlife communities. Our familiar garden birds lived alongside us in a countryside which we have exploited for many centuries in low-intensity, traditional seasonal cycles. Meadows, scrub and many wetlands would eventually disappear if left unmanaged as the natural ecological succession of plants progressively took over. So in fact most of our so-called 'natural' bird habitats and communities were largely defined and maintained by our own activities. This is why changes in those activities are of such importance to birds and a prime concern of bird and wildlife conservationists.

From a bird's point of view, the natural environment of the British Isles has two particularly important characteristics. One is a low diversity of native plants, especially trees. Our wildlife habitats were more or less swept clean by a cataclysmic ice age, a very recent event in ecological terms. As the glaciers retreated, plants and animals recolonised from the south until meltwater filled the Channel and halted their advance. This is why we now have fewer native species of tree, for example, than Americans at the same latitude. The other key feature of the habitat is our variable weather which is strongly seasonal and unpredictable from day to day within that regular cycle. Tropical forests have relatively predictable weather and an amazing diversity of plants. They support hundreds of bird species, many of which are specialists with very particular foods or 'microhabitats'. By comparison, we have relatively few resident bird species but they tend to be very versatile and adaptable, exploiting many different resources and surviving fluctuating conditions.

Biogeographers specialise in recording and understanding habitat distributions. Using techniques such as identifying excavated ancient pollen, they conclude that Oak trees covered much of Britain for most of the last few thousand years, following the Birch and Scots Pine northwards as the climate improved. Ancient Oak forests are not uniform like modern tree plantations but provide a wonderful diversity of habitats among which our 'native' bird

This thousand year old Oak wood is not a murky, impenetrable tangle but light and open. Traditional management maintains diversity, just like a large garden!

communities developed and most of our familiar garden birds were truly at home. Under the giant trees, forest floors were relatively open and light in winter when a deep, warm leaf litter protected plenty of worms and other invertebrates. Later in the year bluebells and brambles fed insects, provided nest sites and autumn fruit while a shrubby layer of holly and small native trees increased the variety of feeding and nesting opportunities. Fallen trees filled up with nutritious grubs as they rotted and made large sunny clearings with scrub and seeding herbacious plants. Enormous numbers of leaf-eating caterpillars fed songbird nestlings in spring.

As human communities settled, this habitat did not stay natural for long. Many forests were managed for grazing and timber, using traditional practices such as small scale rotational coppicing, but these activities tended to increase the variety of resources on offer for birds rather than make the forest more uniform. Even as the forests were cleared, more habitat diversity was provided for birds when crops were grown in small fields full of weeds and insects, usually by the same communities that consumed them. Livestock grazed on commons, many of which were later enclosed with carefully tended thick hedgerows. Winter was a grim season for humans living on whatever could be stored without refrigeration but relatively benign for birds with the shelter of the forests, rich stores of weed seeds in the fields and fruit in the hedges. Even during the agricultural boom of the late nineteenth century, when more land was ploughed than ever before or since, woodlands, crop rotations and hedgerows were integral parts of the thriving rural economy.

Because our birds are versatile and adaptable species, they took advantage of the additional habitat diversity provided by humans to prosper, despite our small variety of native plants and our variable weather. They exploited the mosaic of different resources provided in our patchwork countryside in different ways at different times of year. Their lives are dominated by seasonal cycles, moving from one resource to the next as the weather changes. Caterpillars in spring, spiders in summer, fruit in autumn, seeds in winter. Holes for nesting, shrubs for feeding, scrub for hiding while moulting, clearings or field edges for foraging. Conserving these birds is not simply a matter of preserving one particular resource. We need to identify all the different resources that birds exploit at different times of year and make sure the seasonal cycle is not broken by a 'missing link'. Finches may feed in fields but if hedges are removed they lose their nest sites. Tits may nest in boxes on buildings but remove native trees and there are no caterpillars for the young.

Seasonal cycles of habitat use can be seen in many of the Garden BirdWatch reporting rate graphs which are printed for each species in this booklet. Gardens are one piece of the available habitat mosaic. Birds exploit them when they most need to and leave them at times of year when other habitats are more appropriate or productive. To help birds effectively in gardens and throughout the year we need to provide as many different resources as possible, appropriate to each season.

Even though clearances and enclosures destroyed most of the forests over the last few hundred years, the traditional patchy landscape established since Roman times could still be recognised in the 1940s. Since then the pace of change has greatly accelerated in the countryside. Powerful selective weedkillers have transformed fields into highly efficient monocultures, much of which will feed intensively reared animals. Chemicals allow land to be cropped all year with no winter stubbles left and no need for a fallow period. Many hedges have been destroyed or at best neglected. Artificially fertilised silage is cut two or even three times a year, supporting far fewer invertebrates than traditional meadows. Farming is driven by international rules and subsidies rather than local community needs.

Intensive farming may not be a bad thing in itself. The global human population will double by about 2050, so more efficient farming may be the only way to feed ourselves while protecting truly wild countryside. But for birds, traditional mosaic landscapes replaced the diversity of resources lost when forests were destroyed with many different kinds of sesonal food and cover. Modern land management tends towards uniformity and continuous production, overriding traditional cycles.

In modern arable landscapes a garden may provide the only oasis of songbird habitat among miles of hedgeless 'agridesert'.

This reduces the range of different habitat resources, each of which might have been essential for one or more species of wild bird at some particular time of year.

Gardens are potentially a good refuge for birds threatened by deterioration of our traditional countryside. They are organised into small patches, with many transitions between different management styles. But in general they tend to be less attractive from a bird's point of view for several important reasons. Diversity of habitat structures and heights is low, large trees are unpopular in housing estates and few gardeners have the space for a dense patch of impenetrable scrub. Constant disturbance by gardeners, pets and children is a real problem, especially for breeding birds. Most garden plants are alien species, supporting few invertebrates so many nestlings starve. Gardens tend to be too tidy, lacking leaf litter or dead wood and chemical use is still generally high, destroying vital food resources and even poisoning birds. Providing food and nest sites can greatly improve a garden for birds but it is also important to bear in mind how their original habitat would have looked and what is being lost in the countryside. Then we can plan and manage our gardens to replace as many of the missing links in the birds' seasonal cycles as possible.

Habitats

In the natural world almost anything can be eaten. Even poisonous plants have specialist consumers. The caterpillars of the Cinnabar Moth eat Ragwort and become toxic themselves, but are still relished by Cuckoos. Oak trees are eaten alive by insects, predators carry parasites and are consumed by scavengers after death. Somewhere on Earth a bird has evolved to exploit almost any food you could name but although geese can eat grass, smaller birds are prevented by their lifestyle and metabolism from relying on inefficient, heavy or nutrient-poor foods.

The main problem is flying, which means birds must stay as light as possible at all times and need huge amounts of energy to power their hyperactive wing muscles. So they favour the most efficient foods which provide the most nutrients for the least weight and shortest handling time. They also have incredibly fast digestions:

'Sunflower hearts' are a very efficient food for small birds, high protein, high energy and virtually zero handling time as they are already shelled.

a thrush can ingest, digest and excrete fruit in as little as eleven minutes!

If a resource is reliably available all year, birds can afford to specialise on it. In warmer climates, Hummingbirds can depend on nectar, Oilbirds on palm nuts. Migration between climates can also enable specialisation. Swallows, Swifts and martins must leave us when flying insects, their specialised food, disappear in autumn. It still makes sense for them to fly back all that way in spring as relatively few of our resident birds compete for their unusual nest sites.

Among our resident garden bird species very few are genuine specialists, only the Sparrowhawk really depends on one particular type of food, smaller birds. Tawny Owls are predators too of course but take a much wider range of prey than is often realised, literally anything from ants to rabbits. The young owls are driven from the nesting territory by their parents in late summer which is a particularly difficult time for them to find easy prey such as earthworms and beetles. Many starve. Treecreepers and Goldcrests may not look like voracious hunters but they resort to vegetarian fare only very reluctantly. Tiny seeds of pine and spruce are eaten in cold weather. Russian Treecreepers' diets include up to 30% vegetable matter in their desperately hard winters and even ours will peck grimly at a bit of soft bread in a dire emergency, as will our otherwise largely insectivorous Wrens.

It may seem that some of our birds are specialist seed-eaters but in fact only pigeons and doves are totally vegetarian. Their nestlings do not need invertebrates as the adults secrete 'crop milk' which provides enough protein for the very rapid growth of the young. Breeding is very demanding for birds, hatchlings need vast amounts of protein in an extremely short time. While naked in a nest they are vulnerable to predation, weather and infections. They need to fly freely and keep themselves warm as soon as possible, which means increasing their weight several times over in just a few days and growing a full set of feathers. So even sparrows, which live almost entirely on seeds throughout the year as adults, must have access to plenty of high-protein invertebrates for those crucial first few days of their lives.

Most of our common garden birds are versatile opportunists rather than specialists, varying their diet according to what is available in season. The classic examples are thrushes such as Blackbirds which eat almost entirely invertebrates in spring and early summer and almost entirely fruit in autumn and winter. Of course, these adaptable birds always take advantage of an out-of-season treat. Put mealworms out in November or strawberries in March and you will see the ecological versatility of the Blackbird demonstrated! Other birds however, while clearly varying their natural diet according to the seasons, are harder to help in a garden setting particularly those which favour small weed seeds such as Tree Sparrows or open country like Skylarks. Linnets seem very reluctant to visit gardens despite their adaptability to captivity. Bullfinches and buntings really ought to be easier to attract to bird tables than they are. There's obviously more to it than peanuts.

An intelligent approach to helping garden birds involves more than hanging nuts up in winter and hoping for the best. Taking it for granted that we provide water as well, which is just as important as food all year round, we can then consider the different needs of the different birds in the various seasons and the state of our local 'natural' habitats. For example, if you are surrounded by 'agridesert' of autumn-sown cereal and flailed hedges, Yellowhammers and Greenfinches will be very short of seeds in spring and early summer. Black sunflower seeds may make the difference between successful breeding and disappearance from the area. If your garden is in the middle of a huge new estate, surrounded by tidy-minded insecticide users, even Blackbirds may have trouble rearing young unless the adults are sustained with sunflower hearts or chopped peanuts, so they can spare the few invertebrates they do find for their nestlings. Better still, provide a few mealworms.

Resources for birds appear to be generally declining in the countryside, but thoughtful garden provisioning during the breeding season and summer can help to compensate by greatly improving the chances of successful nesting in our gardens, especially if linked with an invertebrate-friendly gardening regime. This means drastically reducing pesticides, using natural

Even shy species respond to appropriate foods.

composts, choosing native plants and tidying less, to foster worms, spiders, beetles and ideally as many snails as you can 'farm' to feed the disappearing Song Thrush.

The next step is to try to emulate the diverse structure of a mosaic countryside, reducing the impact of competition on the shyer bird species. A tiny plot can provide diversity vertically with ground cover plants, shrubs and small trees, some feeders hung high and some food on the ground. Even hanging baskets can hide bird feeders! Put some food near cover and some in a more open situation, watching out for cats. Distract larger birds with scraps on the lawn while secreting grated cheese and niger seed under shrubs for Dunnocks and Wrens. In summer, observe where birds feed naturally, in winter distribute small feeders in those locations rather than centralising. Put feeders right inside bushes or hedges if Sparrowhawks are trying to make a living in your neighbourhood as well. Although it is fun to watch the birds eating (and we are trying to count them) bear in mind that feeding garden birds is not primarily a spectator sport but an attempt to help them!

When friends and neighbours find out you have volunteered as a garden bird 'citizen scientist', they often assume you know everything about feeding birds. In fact the only thing you can be sure of about birds is that they can't read bird books, so they often surprise 'experts' with unexpected behaviours. However we will always be happy to send your neighbours a general information sheet on garden bird feeding, and here are some suggested answers to questions they might ask.

Garden BirdWatch 'Top Ten Tips'

1. *Only put out as much food as is consumed in a day or two. Never allow food or detritus to accumulate. Reduce the food at quiet times.*
2. *Keep feeders reasonably clean and move them around the garden periodically, to avoid infectious droppings building up in one place.*
3. *In the nesting season avoid presenting whole peanuts. Chop them, or use a mesh feeder from which adult birds can only take small fragments.*
4. *Try to have reasonably clean water available at all times for bathing as well as drinking but never add salt or any chemicals in winter.*
5. *Don't put out salted snacks, highly-flavoured foods, uncooked rice, whole bacon rinds or unsoaked dessicated coconut which can be fatal to birds.*
6. *Keep food away from any cover in which cats might lurk and consider electronic scarers, which need relocating weekly for best results.*
7. *..but, if Sparrowhawks are present, place feeders next to shrubs to allow birds to escape. Clip the shrubs back hard at the base so cats can't hide.*
8. *Provide a wide variety of different foods in different positions and types of feeder. Try offering unmixed foods separately rather than mixtures.*
9. *Cereal grain such as wheat attracts pigeons. Use better quality pure foods such as black sunflower seeds or peanuts if they are a problem.*
10. *Stick to natural foods, rather than chemically altered or processed foods such as margarine. Vegetarians, try oats mixed with oil for winter fat.*

Food

Pioneer ethologists such as Konrad Lorenz showed in the 1930s how the reasons for animals' behaviour could often be established by careful observations and simple experiments. Behavioural studies have since contributed greatly to understanding and hence to helping wild birds. For example, 'game theory' considers the reactions of individuals to the various behaviours of others. This may seem of little conservation value but in fact observing birds competing with each other is another way of inferring their overall conservation status from a sample population.

Ethologists study the survival benefits of behaviours to individuals, hence explaining their selection by evolution over millions of years and taking care to avoid 'anthropomorphism' (projecting human motivations onto other species). A Blue Tit's brain is the size of a pea; they don't have the wiring to experience life in the complex way that we do. Foraging and fighting for food, constantly risking death from cold or predation, birds can't afford the luxury of inefficient or unproductive behaviour. Every behaviour is a trade-off between the fundamental requirements of feeding, breeding and surviving and is the best compromise for that species for that season, weather and time of day. Birds need acute senses, of temperature, daylength and geography as well as of sight and hearing to make these judgements. The penalty for getting it even slightly wrong may be death.

Tropical Tree Sparrows with food constantly available can breed successfully for up to nine months of the year. In our temperate climate, seasonal cycles influence bird behaviour, triggering mating, nesting, moulting and winter survival strategies at different times. Day length is a fundamental variable but the birds must also react appropriately to short-term variations in weather and food availability within the basic yearly cycle. The timing of behaviours can be critical. Tits must lay their first eggs at exactly the right time so the clutch hatches just when the first flush of leaf-eating caterpillars appears in Oak trees. If they leave it too late, the Oak leaves build up high levels of tannins which depress the caterpillar population and the brood may starve. Temperature cues seem vital in getting this timing right.

Breeding involves complex and extraordinary behaviours, including singing which either attracts a mate or proclaims a territory, depending on the species. Even closely-related birds sing for different reasons. The Song Thrush, hard to see in woods, sings to attract a mate and goes quiet once successful.

This young Chaffinch must learn quickly how long to spend bathing, among all the the other behaviours essential for survival. Like most resources, water is in limited supply. Access to it will be largely determined by competition.

Redwings are sociable and nest in more open country so finding a mate is easier. Their song proclaims a breeding territory. Many birds have a range of different songs and calls for different purposes. The dawn chorus is a good example of a complex behavioural compromise. Poor light means that although birds are hungry, feeding is inefficient as food is hard to see. But gloom offers a good opportunity to enter a neighbour's territory, especially as many birds are killed by predators at night so it may well be vacant. Displaying will be ineffective until the light improves but a loud song proclaims continued residence and repels boarders.

Reproduction becomes the overwhelming preoccupation whenever birds sense that conditions offer a good chance of success. For pigeons and doves, this can mean virtually the whole year round!

Many birds have evolved the abilities to copy and learn among their behavioural repertoires. Some species learn their songs from their parents, sometimes starting to listen while they are still in the egg. It can take them considerable practice to get it right. Great Tits are renowned for working out novel ways of getting at food, behaviours which are reinforced by a successful outcome and subsequently copied by others. Migrants learn details of their routes. Experimental translocation of migrant birds to unfamiliar locations suggests that first year birds set off in a more or less correct direction by inherited instinct but subsequently return by remembering major landmarks and a quite complex ' memory map' of their home area.

The annual moult in late summer is probably the part of a bird's life cycle least familiar to garden bird enthusiasts because while moulting, birds change their behaviour to conserve energy and keep a low profile. Replacing the plumage is very demanding and their ability to fly is slightly impaired making them more vulnerable to predators, so they spend as much time as possible feeding and resting inconspicuously. Constantly battered in bushes and exposed to all weathers, plumage simply wears out after a while and so adult passerines replace all their feathers every year. First year passerines moult into adult plumage at the same time but most species retain their juvenile flight feathers. This conserves energy and perhaps saves the inexperienced youngsters from becoming even more vulnerable to predators. Long-tailed Tits are a curious exception, juveniles replacing all their feathers. This could be because they are related to tropical birds which do not have to conserve so much energy yet it does not seem to affect their survival, perhaps because they forage so efficiently in flocks and keep each other warm in winter.

B irds are constantly on the move within habitats, feeding themselves and their young, defending territory, finding nest materials or perhaps escaping from a predator but their unique ability to fly enables them to move quickly between quite different habitats as well. Many species take advantage of this to exploit seasonal resources not available to less mobile animals, for example waders and wildfowl can spend summer breeding in the high arctic where very few creatures can survive the winter. Migratory birds alternate between two habitats, sometime calling in at others on the way. Insect-eaters like Swallows are 'obligate' migrants. They could not survive our cool wet winters when their food is not available, so have evolved an inherited long-distance migration instinct, evacuating one region and transferring their entire population to another according to an annual rhythm.

More versatile seed-eaters such as the Goldfinch are 'partial migrants'. They will not make the extra effort of a long journey if there is still food to be had at home. Each bird only flies as far south as it needs to find food. Dominant individuals monopolise the nearest available food, forcing the youngest birds to travel the furthest. Some partial migrants visit us in winter when even our weather is an improvement on that in their northern breeding areas. The movements of these birds such as Siskins, Bramblings, Fieldfares and Redwings vary greatly with food supply and temperatures but the

An automatic camera in a nestbox records this Coal Tit's continuous movement, adding up to a spectacular distance travelled each day, constantly risking predation.

underlying pattern of regular migration is fairly consistent although it can change slowly over time. For example, more and more Siskins now breed in Britain. From time to time, when winter food supplies are very low in north-eastern Europe, we experience exceptional influxes of birds, known as irruptions. As well as unusually large numbers of those species that normally winter with us, irruptions can bring us continental birds which do not necessarily cross the North Sea regularly every year such as Great Spotted Woodpeckers, Crossbills and Waxwings.

Another kind of seasonal movement is dispersal, when young birds leave their breeding areas to set up home elsewhere. Most gardens suddenly go quiet in late summer; the young birds have dispersed and the remaining adults keep a very low profile during their annual moult. In very territorial species, if a youngster cannot find a vacant territory it may have to travel a long way, even overseas, to survive its first winter. Even for resident species, finding enough food can require substantial movements in autumn and winter. Many birds that pair off to breed regroup afterwards into flocks, ranging around large areas. Young sparrows and finches traditionally flocked to autumn stubble fields on farmland. Tits of different species often flock together to work a regular feeding 'beat' each winter's day. Although many of these movements are seasonal and regular they are not described as migrations as they do not shift the geographic 'centre of gravity' of the species.

Understanding the movement patterns of birds is clearly very important for conservation. A migrant bird that is declining might have problems overseas or on route and, unless we know where they go, there would be little we could do. Disappearing stubble fields could leave birds short of food at an important stage of their annual movement cycle, perhaps causing them to return to gardens or to enter winter in poor condition with consequently reduced survival. New foods

provided in gardens could save some birds the trouble of having to fly south at all! Some of the most interesting results we can derive from your Garden BirdWatch records are the weekly average reporting rate graphs, included for each species in this booklet. These show regular seasonal cycles in most birds' use of gardens.

Ringing juveniles, like this Goldfinch, provides accurate survival data as the age and origin of the bird are known.

Much of what we know about migration and movement has been learnt from the efforts of specially trained volunteers marking birds with tiny, lightweight numbered leg rings. There are scientific bird ringing schemes in most developed countries. The BTO issues the rings and receives any that are found and sent in by the public for both Britain and Ireland. Recently the emphasis of bird ringing projects has shifted from studying migration to examining another very important conservation issue: how long wild birds are surviving. If the average survival time of adult birds were changing this could obviously affect populations. At 'constant effort' bird ringing sites, licensed volunteers catch birds harmlessly in very fine 'mist nets' each summer. The numbers and positions of these nets and the length of time for which they are put out is kept the same from year to year. This produces an accurate sample of the bird population at that site and birds retrapped each year are carefully recorded for survival analysis. The proportions of young and adult birds caught each year shows whether breeding success at that site is varying, which is critical to understanding the underlying causes of any declines. For this to work at all, ringers have to take great care that their own activities at a site do not affect bird survival or breeding.

Most birds occur in more than one country and have 'common' names in several different languages, but their 'scientific' names are standardised internationally. About 1.7 million living organisms have been formally 'described' somewhere in the scientific literature and their relationships to other organisms investigated in order to allocate a two-part name according to a system developed by the 18th century Swedish biologist Linnaeus. Most common European birds have relatively simple scientific names devised by Linnaeus himself in Latin, still a practical language of international communication for scientists at that time.

For example, *Passer domesticus* literally means House Sparrow, with Latin reversing the two words of course. *Passer* is Latin for sparrow and denotes a small group of related birds called a **genus**. All true sparrows belong to this genus and hence the first word of their scientific names is the same. *Domesticus* identifies our 'domestic' sparrow uniquely as a single **species** within the genus *Passer*.

Other birds in the genus *Passer* include the species that we call the Tree Sparrow. In German this bird is called the 'field sparrow', in Dutch the 'ring sparrow' and the American Tree Sparrow is a completely different species! But anywhere in the world you can use its scientific name, *Passer montanus* (which literally means mountain sparrow!) and be sure which bird you and the local enthusiasts are discussing.

Scientific names form part of a hierarchy or 'family tree' which describes the relationships or 'taxonomy' of all known organisms. The true sparrows of the genus *Passer* are related to the rock sparrows of the genus *Petronia*, within a single **family** of birds called the *Passeridae*. This family joins many other families of birds in a larger group called an **order**, in this case the *Passeriformes* (sparrow-like birds), often known as 'passerines'.

Taxonomists periodically adjust our 'family tree' of birds as better evidence about their relationships accumulates. In fact Linnaeus himself originally named the Tree Sparrow *Fringilla montana* believing it to be a species of finch but after only eight years this error was corrected. Many people ask why bird books do not list birds alphabetically by their English names. It is much more biologically meaningful to present birds in order of their evolutionary relationships and all serious bird books and reports follow this 'systematic order'. It is difficult to summarise complex evolutionary relationships in a simple sequence but, for example, Divers and Grebes are placed together at the beginning of the list. These birds are closely related to each other but they are both only distantly related to the passerines, which are placed at the end. Today, molecular biology usefully supplements taxonomists' traditional investigations of anatomy and behaviour.

Bird Taxonomy (simplified!)

Order:
e.g. Passeriformes

|

Family:
e.g. Passeridae

|

Genus:
e.g. Passer

|

Species:
e.g. Passer domesticus

Names

To identify a new bird: ask somebody.

For a scientific bird survey to work, correct identification of our study species is obviously important. If you are concerned about identifying any of the birds in your garden the best way to learn is to ask advice. Genuine bird enthusiasts always try to help beginners but like all communication, sharing the details of a bird is easier if you use a common language. Your bird identification book should include a drawing showing the accepted names of the different parts of birds, usually labelled 'bird topography'. Try comparing pictures of birds with that drawing and see if you can pick up some of the language from these examples. A Brambling has a white **rump**, a Great Spotted Woodpecker has a red **vent**. Robins have a red **breast**, Redwings have red **flanks**. Siskins have a pale **belly**. Young Greenfinches have some yellow on their **primaries**, but young Goldfinches show yellow on their **secondaries** as well. A Blue Tit has a blue **crown**, but a Blackcap has a black (or brown) **cap**. Coal Tits have a white **nape**, Tree Sparrows have a white **collar**.

Even young birds, like these streaky Greenfinches, may show you a diagnostic plumage feature if you are patient.

Most birds have so-called 'diagnostic' plumage features. Learn as many as you can but don't be discouraged if you can't memorise details. Instead, remember the term 'jizz' which derives from 'general impression, size and shape'. Experienced observers separate birds (dragonflies, bats, aeroplanes, and even people!) on 'jizz' most of the time, and this is the skill to aim for as plumage details do vary and can be hard to see clearly on a fast-moving bird.

Many people find recognising bird songs a challenge, including experienced enthusiasts. Unless you have lots of time to watch birds singing, contact BTO sales and buy a CD or tape. Don't try to memorise the recordings exactly, this is difficult and discouraging and birds sing 'dialects' in different areas. Concentrate instead on the tone or timbre of each bird and associate them with other sounds. For example: if a Great Tit is a squeaky door, a Coal Tit is a squeaky sandal. If a Woodpigeon hoots like the Flying Scotsman, a Collared Dove toots like the 8.20. Gain confidence (and impress friends!) with simple 'tricks'. A Song Thrush repeats every phrase at least twice and a Chaffinch generally ends its song with a distinctive chirpy flourish. Think of the 'character' of the call — does it match the 'character' of the bird? Or match the 'style' of the song with a musical performer.

Try these ..

Crow:	*dour, no-nonsense*	*Blackbird:*	*Placido Domingo*
Rook:	*talkative, sociable*	*Robin:*	*James Galway*
Magpie:	*sinister, cackling*	*Wren:*	*Nigel Kennedy*
Jay:	*busy, peevish*	*Blackcap:*	*John Coltrane*
Jackdaw:	*elfin, spooky*	*Dunnock:*	*the Singing Postman*

If a birdwatcher never goes anywhere without binoculars, an ornithologist never goes anywhere without binoculars and a notebook. And don't forget the pencil! Recording the birds you see systematically and combining your data with those of many other volunteers as part of a BTO survey can really contribute to conservation. But even bird records collected more casually and one-off notes of unusual species or vagrants can help our understanding of bird movements and biodiversity if they are sent to your County Bird Recorder. Most counties publish an annual bird report listing the species recorded over the year and any unusual events. Arrivals and departures of migrants also interest county recorders and some counties have study projects for particular bird families for which all records are welcomed.

Even your records of the birds seen in the garden, particularly migrants or less common species, will be accepted with interest by your county recorder and carefully filed but if you do want to take part in the fun of local biological recording it is really essential to compile your observations into what is known as 'systematic order' before forwarding them. All your various records of dates, locations and numbers for each individual species should be compiled together, species by species. Then these groups of single-species records should be arranged in the same order of related families and species that is used in any reputable bird book. Don't submit your Garden BirdWatch 'diary' records of mixed species in date order or use alphabetical order of common names and don't necessarily expect a personal reply as county recorders are also unpaid volunteers doing the job in their spare time. But if your records are used for the bird report, you should see your name in it!

Local arrangements for recording birds vary, some county recorders can even accept computer disks. In large counties the work is often split between several volunteers or clubs, but generally a county Bird Club or Natural History Society listed in The BirdWatcher's Yearbook (see page 76) will be in overall charge. They all welcome enquiries, even from beginners. If you cannot contact them, try asking at the county museum or your RSPB group meeting. BTO members can consult the volunteer BTO Regional Representative for your area (SAE always appreciated if you write) who should be able to provide you with details of your local bird recorder. Often they are one and the same busy person! Contributing to local records can become addictive. Many counties also have recorders for mammals, plants and fungi, various kinds of insects or aquatic creatures, even algae and slugs!

County Bird Reports, always interesting reading.

20

Fierce-looking hawk with gleaming yellow eye. Sparrowhawk has less pointed wings than smaller Kestrel and never hovers. Hunts among trees, bushes, small gardens, Kestrel prefers open ground. Kestrel breast is streaked vertically, Sparrowhawk's is barred horizontally.

43,000 pairs. Figures given in these columns are total estimated numbers of breeding pairs in Britain and Ireland unless otherwise stated.

The wild creatures from whom we borrow our gardens are not pets but visitors from another world, the natural world. In their world, every birth and death is connected in a vast, interlocking web of recycling energy, an ecosystem. Over timescales that defy our comprehension, ecosystems evolve a finely-tuned balance.

One method of studying an ecosystem is to analyse the food chains in which each creature is an important link. Garden birds are near the tops of food chains based on green plants. These absorb the sun's energy and nutrients from soil, producing seeds, leaves to feed caterpillars and compost to feed worms, in turn sustaining

It is unusual for Sparrowhawks to enter a building but this juvenile was found in a stable, probably waiting to be fed by its parents. The 'scalloping' on the wing feathers and general 'untidiness' are typical of very young hawks, in fact this one still has specks of down visible on its breast.

songbirds such as tits and thrushes. Above them in the food chain is the Sparrowhawk, a specialist predator which depends on a healthy ecosystem producing a surplus of smaller birds to feed its own youngsters. Eventually it too dies and is recycled to feed the plants. In fact thanks to us the Sparrowhawk is now at the top of the food chain, with virtually no natural predators left in the British Isles although a very hungry female in winter may kill and eat her smaller mate. There is no room for sentiment in the natural world! The most significant predators of Sparrowhawks are Goshawks and Pine Martens, both very rare due to human persecution.

In the British Isles we have become accustomed to seeing far fewer hawks than would naturally be present. Birds of prey were systematically persecuted before the introduction of legal protection, and the remaining populations were drastically reduced by pesticide poisoning in the late 1950s. Finally, populations of Sparrowhawks appear to be returning to natural levels and we would expect that from now on their numbers will once more closely reflect the fortunes of the small birds on which they depend. This implies that monitoring Sparrowhawk numbers will be an effective and meaningful method of monitoring the overall health and productivity of the whole food chain, including songbirds. If songbirds become scarcer or produce fewer surplus young then we might expect the population of

White stripe above eye. Male small as Collared Dove, blue-grey above, white barred with apricot below, dark bars on grey tail. Female larger, brown above, finely barred grey on white below, large evenly-spaced dark tail bars. Goshawk is much bigger, shy and rare.

21

Sparrowhawks to decrease quite quickly in response. Indeed there are indications that they are now declining again in some areas. In general, large predators are fewer and more visible and so should be easier to monitor than their smaller, more widespread prey. However a problem with using Sparrowhawk numbers as an indicator of the health of the ecosystem is that these birds are elusive and secretive in their natural woodland habitat, and so in fact are quite hard to count. Monitoring their visits to gardens, where they are relatively easy to spot, may well become a very useful and effective contribution. The dependence of Sparrowhawks on smaller birds was illustrated by Professor Ian Newton who found that the first Sparrowhawk eggs are not laid until 5-10 days after they first start to catch fledgling songbirds, even though their nests are often ready several weeks earlier. Weather also affects them, particularly rain which can reduce their hunting success by a third.

One of the most intriguing aspects of Sparrowhawk biology is the size difference between the sexes, the largest such difference in any bird of prey. Each sex specialises in a different range of prey species, maximising their total intake. The male is too small to incubate the eggs, so the female depends on him to feed her for a whole month or even longer. She dare not leave her nest as Sparrowhawk eggs are very attractive to predators. Each is about half the size of a hen's egg and a makes a good meal for a Jay or squirrel. Smaller males are more vulnerable to cold winters. In many areas there is a surplus of females, competing strongly for the surviving males with the best hunting territories.

Predators and their prey must evolve a balance or they could not both persist and research confirms that songbird numbers fluctuate more or less independently of Sparrowhawk numbers. There was no great upsurge in songbirds when hawks disappeared and no great decline of their favourite prey species when they returned. This does not necessarily mean that Sparrowhawks could not seriously affect a prey species which had become rare or could not adapt to a changing environment. Sparrowhawks are probably the main reason why the numerous brightly-coloured Budgerigars which escape into the wild each year fail to establish a breeding population!

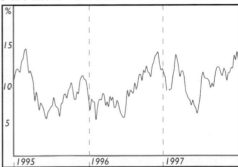

Plotting the percentage of Garden BirdWatchers who report each of the survey species week by week indicates how the different birds use our gardens at different times of the year. Over the first three complete years of Garden BirdWatch the Sparrowhawk reporting rate is fairly constant and it is hard to see any obvious seasonal pattern. The apparent slight rise in 1997 could be misleading, as bird populations can vary dramatically between years. We will need several more years' data to tell whether there is any genuine long-term trend. Dashed lines mark the start of each new calendar year.

Steady recovery over last 40 years after persistent pesticides seriously affected breeding. Now declining again in some areas.

22

Small gull, size of Collared Dove. From Common Gull by orangey-red legs, red bill with dark tip, dark chocolate brown cap in summer or dark smudges on white head in winter, which is when it most often visits gardens. Juvenile birds have some mottled brown wing feathers

210,000 pairs. About 12% of world population, breeding widely over most of the British Isles although sparser in south-west England.

Few urban gardeners are surprised to see Black-headed Gulls in a hard winter, diving down to snatch scraps from bird tables or scuffling for bread in the park. However this represents a major change in the winter behaviour of this bird over little more than a hundred years, which is a short time in biology. The first significant numbers of Black-headed Gulls wintering in London were only seen at the end of the last century. Since these few pioneer birds discovered the rich pickings available

in urban areas the species has become a regular winter visitor to many towns and cities and apparently in ever-increasing numbers. Their behaviour is still changing, with more and more birds staying inland to breed. Previously coastal wetlands were their favoured nesting habitat. We may well see this continuing change reflected in garden records of this species. So far, these still show a strong weather-dependent winter peak. Seabird population monitoring is coordinated by the

Winter birds can be confusing as they are not black-headed! Legs and bill are more orange than red, head is smudgy. Brown feathers indicate a young bird.

Joint Nature Conservation Committee. Their work suggests that Black-headed Gulls are slowly increasing and hence are not of conservation concern.

Professor Niko Tinbergen helped to establish ethology, the science of animal behaviour. Black-headed Gulls were the subjects of some of his pioneering studies, demonstrating that the purposes of apparently obscure animal behaviours could be determined by careful observations and non-destructive experiments. For example, a series of clever experiments showed that the gulls remove eggshells from their

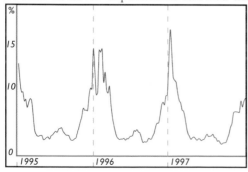

nests to keep them camouflaged but do not advertise hatching in this way until their chicks have dried out, when they are less vulnerable to neighbouring gulls. This kind of work shows that animals evolve complex behaviour patterns with many compromises, trading off one threat against another. Monitoring changes in gull behaviour is of practical importance, as well as interest. Some larger species have now started nesting rather noisily on houses!

The Black-headed Gull is still largely a winter visitor to relatively few gardens It will be important to monitor any changes in this pattern.

Black-headed Gull Larus ridibundus

Generally plain pinkish buff, greyer below. Dark bill and eye, white eye ring. Tail has white corners above, black and white pattern below. Adults have unique black collar, edged with white. Clear, persistent three-note song 'coo COO cuh' and strange 'eeer, eeer' flight call.

The recent spread of the Collared Dove has been one of the most extraordinary spontaneous changes in the international distribution of a wild creature that we have been able to observe in modern times. Following a very rapid expansion across Europe the first birds were recorded in the British Isles as recently as 1953. Since then the species has spread westward right through Britain, Ireland and has even been reported in Iceland. In only 45 years our population has increased from zero to the present estimate of about a quarter of a million pairs. Interestingly, this is less than one tenth of the estimated population of Woodpigeons. Yet the Collared Dove is regularly reported in around three quarters of our gardens compared to only half our Garden BirdWatchers reporting the larger native species. Also, the garden reporting rate varies less between seasons. This might support the suggestion that gardens are important in enabling Collared Doves to spread so rapidly and indeed it is still relatively unusual to see them far from gardens in the countryside.

It is hard but possible to sex some Collared Doves in breeding plumage, males are generally pinker and their collars more contrasty. Try to get your eye in whenever the birds give you a clue (see page 14!) Juveniles look 'scalloped' with light edges to feathers.

Many questions remain to be answered about Collared Doves. Will they stay in gardens and parks, associated with human habitation like House Sparrows? Or will they spread out into woodland and farmland? Have they displaced any native species? Or do they exploit a vacant niche, as seems to be the case with the introduced Little Owl? How important is garden feeding to their survival and continuing increase? Are they an economically significant pest that should be 'controlled'?

Evolutionary biologists suggest that the rapid expansion was due to a genetic mutation affecting the birds' direction of seasonal movement. Analysis of BTO ringing data in 1981 showed that our Collared Doves do have a clear preference for moving north-west. We would now expect natural selection to have started reducing this tendency in our population as birds that do not move will have a better chance of survival than those heading out over the Atlantic!

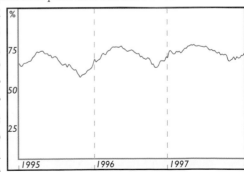

Apparent upward trend and decreasing seasonality may reflect more summer feeding,

Population increased after colonisation in the 1950s but is now levelling out although nesting success still seems to be increasing. 230,000 pairs.

Large, plump, white patch and green smudge on neck. No black wing bars, no black collar. Generally grey, pink breast, black tail tip, bright white flashes on wings in flight. Repeats clear song, 'hoo HOOO hoo hoohoo', often adding extra 'hoo' at end. Juveniles lack white on neck.

3,500,000 pairs. General increase recently as oilseed rape has compensated for decline caused by loss of clover and fallow fields in late 1960s.

W oodpigeons are 'public enemy number one' on arable farms and in many gardens, where they hoover up huge quantities of expensive bird food meant for smaller species and ruthlessly strip any unprotected young brassicas in hard weather. Like a few other so-called 'pest' species they are not wholly protected by the EU Birds Directive and landowners are allowed to destroy them. For this reason

alone it is important to monitor their numbers and learn as much as possible about how they use different habitats at different times of year. We need to be sure that this control policy is appropriate and that their population is sustainable.

However, this species is scientifically as well as economically interesting, a large, versatile and very successful representative of a group of birds with a

Pigeons take up water with the same frightening efficiency as they take in bird seed! They also foul the water with large droppings, it may be necessary to protect bird baths.

number of startling adaptations. Eating dry grain, Woodpigeons need to drink a lot. Next time one is sucking your birdbath dry, notice that it does not have to lift its head to swallow, like a songbird. Even odder is the fact that pigeons feed their young on a kind of 'milk' secreted from their crops. This means they are the only farmland birds that do not require animal food such as insects and caterpillars to feed their nestlings, the 'milk' providing the necessary protein. It will be interesting to compare changes in their numbers and habits with those of the farmland songbirds which depend on a good supply of invertebrates for successful breeding.

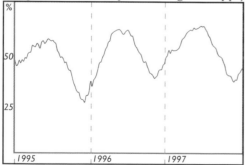

Recent changes in farming may well affect Woodpigeons. The switch from spring-sown to autumn-sown grain may be changing the times at which they can breed. However oilseed rape seems to benefit this species and may be the main cause of an apparent population increase in some areas. Monitoring variations in the numbers of birds in gardens and the seasonal cycles between habitats may throw more light on these interesting and economically important changes.

Woodpigeons visit many gardens in early summer when they are ranging widely to gather food for their young. In autumn they flock on farmland.

Woodpigeon *Columba palumbus*

Town pigeon, many variants, generally dark grey, usually black barring on wings, orange eye, white eye ring, some green or purple sheen on neck. Domestic strains may be brown or white. Bubbling, continuous 'oorh, rooh, coorh' song rather than distinct 'coo' or 'hoo' notes.

25

In every city there are kind-hearted people who share their last crumbs with pigeons, to the despair of those who have to clear droppings, repair stonework and unblock gutters. Feral Pigeons are descended from Rock Doves, truly wild cliff-nesting colonies of which are now confined to the northern isles. They were domesticated for one reason. They are incredibly productive, breeding continuously given warmth and food, which means throughout the year in cities. Transported worldwide as a source of fresh meat, birds escaped, are now globally distributed and still reproducing! Continuous breeding and the close proximity of their unhygienic nests mean that feeding them in cities supports extremely high populations, infested with infectious diseases and parasites.

Feral Pigeons take all kinds of food but will certainly be attracted by low-cost seed mixtures containing wheat or other cereal. Offer only pea-nuts or pure sunflower seeds to discourage them, ideally in hanging feeders which they cannot negotiate. Ground tables can be protected with two-inch mesh chicken wire or any suitable cage that allows smaller birds access. It's all too easy to take pity on a pigeon in a small garden but these are sociable birds and once attracted will bring all their friends! Complaints from neigh-bours and even the council can follow, prevent-ing you from helping smaller, hungrier birds.

Healthy pigeons have bright orange eyes and beautiful metallic sheens, but many city birds look dull and sickly.

There may be too many pigeons in most cities and they are hardly a threatened species but we should not underestimate their role in conservation. What was the first wild bird you fed, or even touched? For many of us it will have been a pigeon. Children are fascinated by them. Urban youngsters might not have access to any other free-living wildlife and the sympathy inspired can benefit scarcer species. In Basle feeding bans were ignored by dedicated pigeon lovers, so official pigeon lofts were installed at which a few birds could be fed by the diehard enthusiasts and their children, while the ban was enforced elsewhere.

Seed-eating pigeons visit gardens the most when they are hungriest, in late spring. Village birds probably prefer fields and farmyards in autumn.

20,000 pairs. Worrying long-term decline and range contraction, although nesting success has improved. **HIGH BTO ALERT**

The 'Wise Old Owl' snoozing well-camouflaged in a tall tree looks quite benign by day but is actually a powerful hunter. We should worry about its decline because like all predators, its fortunes indicate the condition of an entire ecosystem. And of course it is a beautiful bird, probably the largest and most spectacular species that will actually nest in a suburban garden, enlivening winter nights with its spooky calls. Young naturalists are fascinated by the regurgitated pellets from which all

Roosting Tawny Owls are usually quite hard to spot but it's well worth searching your trees carefully if you know they are around.

kinds of remains can be dissected to show that, unlike the specialist Sparrowhawk, Tawny Owls take a wide range of prey. They may forage on your lawn at night for earthworms, listening alertly then hopping forward like a gigantic Blackbird although not as skilful, breaking most of the worms pulled from the ground. In damp weather half the owls' pellets may be brown, fibrous worm remains rather than the normal grey fur and bones. Suburban owls also take roosting Starlings and young Grey Squirrels whereas small rodents are the mainstays in the countryside. Variations in their numbers affect rural Tawny Owl populations.

If these fabulous birds are calling around your garden in November and you have a tall tree, consider providing a 'chimney' nest box (80 cm long, 25 cm square, open top), slung under a branch at 45° or more to horizontal, mimicking a hole in the end of a broken bough. Ensure the bottom has drainage holes and site it at least 2.5 metres above ground. Young

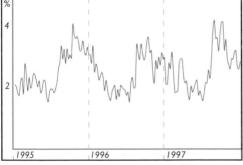

Garden reporting rate is generally low as owls are rarely seen. Regular autumn peak when the birds are calling loudly to proclaim their territories.

owls leave the nest before they can fly and climb around in the trees with their very strong claws like small fluffy monkeys. Sometimes they do fall to the ground: leave them alone as, unlikely though it may sound, they will claw their way back up the tree trunk if undisturbed. If they are threatened by cats or cars, place them as high as you can reach in the tree or nearby bush, the parents will feed them. Wear gloves or they will draw blood for your trouble!

Tawny Owl *Strix aluco*

From any other black and white woodpecker by red vent ('red underpants'). Male has red on back of head, female no red on head at all. Juvenile crown is entirely red, but red vent is duller than adults. Undulating flight, loud 'tchick' call often heard before seen.

27

Of all European woodpeckers, the Great Spotted has the highest proportion of vegetable matter in its diet and among its traditional winter standbys are the seeds of pine trees, extracted from cones by wedging them in tree trunks and hammering out the kernels with the strong bill. Peanuts are similar to pine kernels in texture and composition and these highly intelligent and adaptable woodpeckers have noticed the resemblance. They regularly use hanging nut feeders right through the winter. In early June, when the fledglings leave the nest hole, they are brought to feeders by their parents during a prolonged 'apprenticeship' as various foraging methods from the adults' wide repertoire are demonstrated to them. It is fascinating to watch these exotic and lively youngsters receive peanut-pecking lessons, right outside our windows. The population increased in the 1970s, possibly helped by Dutch Elm disease, but as dead wood is tidied from parks and countryside we can probably expect these birds to turn more and more to gardens for food and even nest sites. Build a large nestbox 40 cm high with a 5 cm diameter hole, and place it high on a secluded tree trunk, having first stuffed it with chunks of expanded polystyrene. If you are lucky, woodpeckers will messily excavate the polystyrene and take up residence.

Males have a red patch on the nape. Juveniles have a red crown, adult females no red on the head at all.

Great Spotted Woodpeckers are beautiful but they specialise in extracting small, succulent, edible creatures from holes in trees and young tits in nestboxes may be on their menu in some areas. You can buy metal plates to fit around the entrance holes but often the woodies will hammer in through the side of the box. Tough boxes, ideally at least an inch thick, are always best. Check your boxes regularly and screw bits of metal or tough plastic over any woodpecker damage as soon as it is noticed, to discourage them. Pieces of a drink can carefully snipped open with strong scissors may be enough if all else fails. Woodpeckers occasionally break into House Martin nests and may be a factor in depressing our population of Willow Tits which like to nest in soft rotten branches and so are rather vulnerable.

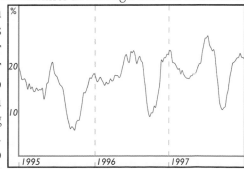

The garden reporting rate peaks in early summer when young birds are taught to use peanut feeders by their parents. In late summer there is plenty of natural food for them in the woods.

Population increased substantially during the 1970s and nesting success seems very high, although natural sites are hard to monitor. **30,000 pairs.**

430,000 pairs. Severe decline along waterways since the mid 1970s may indicate habitat problems.

Wagtails are good examples of bird species which taxonomists subdivide into different races based on plumage variations and their geographical distributions. The resident race of *Motacilla alba* in the British Isles is the Pied Wagtail *Motacilla alba yarrellii*, a familiar bird of parks, larger gardens, motorway service stations and picnic areas. These have dark backs and rumps. Most stay put all year except for northern breeders which winter further south. In autumn and winter Pied Wagtails roost communally, often on buildings or within unlikely man-made structures such as piles of crates. You may notice them leaving your garden in the same direction each afternoon. They approve of the 'Bressingham'

Our resident birds have strongly contrasting blacks and whites, their rumps are dark.

gardening style, island beds providing cover among lawns on which they can forage for insects. Like Robins, they will use a wide range of open-fronted nest boxes and other artificial sites such as planters, trellises and tubs.

In spring and autumn, examine Pied Wagtails carefully. A bird with a paler back, grey rump and cleaner-looking white flanks could be a different race, the White Wagtail *Motacilla alba alba*. White Wagtails migrate, one population breeds mostly in Iceland and winters in west Africa, passing through Ireland and western Britain twice a year. Another population breeds in Norway, a few visit eastern counties on their way to and from south-west France. Juvenile Pied Wagtails look grey but have dark rumps.

In winter, Pied Wagtails feed and roost sociably but dominant birds may also establish feeding territories. Sections of river bank are popular, each bird

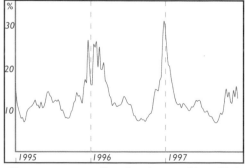

About ten percent of gardens have resident Pied Wagtails, but most reports are during cold spells.

periodically walking round its patch to pick up any food deposited by the water. Careful observations showed how the birds instinctively manage the costs and benefits of sharing these territories. When food is more abundant on a warmer day the territory holder will accept a juvenile 'satellite' bird which helps defend the patch from other birds in exchange for sharing the food. On cold days when food is short, 'satellites' are driven away.

MEDIUM BTO ALERT

Pied Wagtail *Motacilla alba*

Tiny, busy, furtive, cocked tail, brown. Scuttles around in bushes, briefly emerges for a quick look around. Fast, direct whizzing flight from cover to cover. Plumage actually quite intricate with creamy-white stripe above eye. Scolding call, explosive, unbelievably loud trilling song.

29

Wrens buzz around the edges of patios and shrubberies like tiny, brown vacuum cleaners, darting after small insects and gleaning the tiniest crumbs below the bird table. In winter, hunger makes them much bolder and more visible but to really help them it's probably best to introduce a little food into their shady, half-hidden world rather than expect them to stand up to the larger birds at a shared feeding station in the open. Scatter crumbs, a little oatmeal or grated cheese under shrubs and turn the top of the compost heap over to provide both food and a little warmth. These tiny birds are hard to count in the countryside, more often logged by hearing their loud song than by sight. In gardens however they tend to work a fairly regular beat and most observant gardeners know when their Wrens are around. It could be that gathering Wren data from gardens will be one of the most accurate ways of monitoring this species! With patience, most gardeners will sooner or later spot a Wren hopping out onto a rose twig or patio chair, pausing briefly before whizzing off low across the lawn or, if we are lucky, treating us to a blast of amazing song.

Wrens don't often sit still for long, this juvenile is probably waiting to be fed.

In early summer, family parties are quite easy to spot as they twitter noisily to each other while feeding in the border or even the *leylandii*. Many people ask how tiny birds produce such loud songs. Birds do not have vocal chords like ours which are very inefficient, only about two percent of the air passing over them producing sound. Instead they have an organ called the syrinx, just above where their windpipes fork into the two lungs. This is spectacularly efficient, vibrating nearly all the air from the lungs. Even more impressively, it has two halves and can produce two different sounds simultaneously which is why bird songs can sound so complex and richly musical despite being produced on a single 'instrument'.

Wrens' breeding biology is hard to study, their nests are well-concealed and broods cannot be ringed without damaging the domed structure. Males build several nests and the female then chooses the most cryptically concealed of the nests she is offered, in order to best protect her brood from predators.

Wren numbers fluctuate greatly from year to year and are still recovering from the cold spring of 1996 which devastated their breeding.

Wrens are affected by cold winters. Their numbers fluctuate quite dramatically, but generally they seem to be doing fairly well. **9,900,000 pairs.**

For beginners, this can be a confusing 'little brown job', but look out for the thin bill, quite different from sparrow, bunting or finch. Distinctive behaviour, creeps forward along ground like brown mouse, poking about rather anxiously for insects and tiny food scraps.

2,800,000 pairs. A severe decline through the 1980s reduced numbers by more than a third on rural study plots but may be levelling off.

Dunnocks are small brown birds — that's what the name means! As such, their identification troubles beginners, not helped by the fact that they used to be called Hedge Sparrows but actually are not even related to sparrows. In gardens, a rather shy bird feeding quietly on the ground with a thin pointed bill, distinctive mousey movement and the absence of any colours other than streaky brown and grey is pretty certain to be a Dunnock. Given a good view, the only really similar-looking species is the Meadow Pipit, a rural bird of open ground, rarely seen in gardens. These are much brighter underneath, have white edges to their tails and do not generally shuffle about under shrubberies.

We are considered very lucky by Europeans to be able to see Dunnocks so easily in our gardens. Across most of their range they skulk elusively, like small Nightingales, among scrub and woods distant from human habitation. Nobody knows why our Dunnocks are so uniquely confiding. Birds of the genus *Prunella* are called Accentors, and 'officially' our Dunnock has been re-named the Hedge Accentor. This name does not exactly seem to be catching on with the birdwatching public! With the increase in worldwide travel and communication, standardising the English names of birds has become a hot topic. Several familiar species have had their 'official' common names adjusted recently to fall in line with international usage and make exchanging records easier by distinguishing them from different species carrying similar names in other English-speaking countries. Other 'official' English names for our Garden BirdWatch species include Winter Wren, Common Blackbird, Wood Nuthatch, Black-billed Magpie, Eurasian Tree Sparrow and European Greenfinch.

When insects and grubs are plentiful among the leaf litter around bushes they are the Dunnock's preferred food but during the colder months finding enough small seeds becomes this bird's priority. They cannot shell large sunflower seeds without a struggle but seem fond of niger seed, even venturing onto bird tables for it, which is unusual. Sunflower hearts will probably be welcomed if scattered on the ground and breadcrumbs, oatmeal and grated cheese are all taken in emergency.

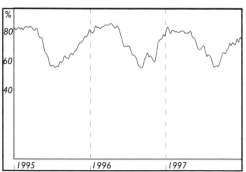

The reporting rate peaks after Christmas as Dunnocks set up their complex 'mating systems'.

Many Dunnocks are polyandrous, which means the females lay eggs fertilised by more than one male. Professor Nick Davies of Cambridge University showed that even more complex 'mating systems' are quite common and in fact only about a third of female Dunnocks are monogamous. This partly depends on how cold the winter has been. More females die in cold winters as males tend to monopolise food, so there are often

Dunnock *Prunella modularis*

Never on hanging feeders, only rarely on tables. Brown upperparts rich streaky chestnut, darker than sandy browns of female House Sparrow. Thundercloud grey breast, musical but rather thin song, surprisingly loud 'tseeep' call. No obvious white patches nor any black bib.

31

extra males in the spring population. It was generally thought that male birds set up territories and females choose between them, but studying Dunnocks revealed that in this species the females compete amongst themselves for territory without reference to the males, which then have to compete with each other to 'move in', a quite different system. A dominant ('alpha') and subordinate ('beta') male whose territories both overlap the larger territory of a female often both join forces with her

The plumage looks drab at a distance but in fact is subtly and richly coloured. Young birds have duller eyes than the adults' bright chestnut but otherwise Dunnocks are hard to tell apart.

and cease to compete, defending the single territory as a trio.

When food is provided the size of females' territories decreases as each bird needs less space. This suggests that in gardens where Dunnocks are artificially fed in winter and during the breeding season, monogamy will be more common as more females will survive and single males will find it easier to monopolise the females with smaller teritories. Although polyandrous trios defend territories as a team, the alpha male guards the female vigorously, trying to stop the beta male from mating with her. The female tries to escape, as a quick liaison with the 'lodger' is in her chicks' interest. Only if the beta male mates with her will he subsequently help to feed them, increasing the brood's chances of fledging successfully.

The Dunnock's specialisation on very tiny prey probably means that any extra help with feeding the young is particularly valuable. This may be one reason why such complex mating behaviour has evolved in this species.

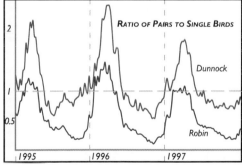

Garden BirdWatch flock size data reflect the differing behaviour of the species. In the breeding season, sociable Dunnocks have to guard their mates assiduously and more gardeners notice pairs than report just single birds. Robins are much more solitary, most gardeners see only one bird at a time except at the very peak of breeding activity in spring. Even then, half of us still only see lone birds. It seems that Robins are allowed out by themselves, but Dunnocks are jealous partners!

MEDIUM BTO ALERT Nest records and ringing suggest that breeding performance improved during the population decline.

Prunella modularis **Dunnock**

Red breast in both sexes is unique among British and Irish birds and easy to spot in garden but can be quite hard to see in dense woods and scrub where often first identified by flutey, musical song, pitched a little higher than Blackbird's. Juvenile lacks red breast, brown upper

6,100,000 pairs. Populations are affected by cold winters but generally increasing over the last ten years. Breeding performance also improving.

Maintaining an official list of English names for our birds is one of the responsibilities of the British Ornithologists Union. Only in 1952 did the BOU adopt 'Robin' as the accepted name for a bird which for several centuries previously had been known as 'Redbreast' or 'Robin Redbreast'. Almost all other European common names for this bird simply mean 'Redbreast' and nobody seems to be quite sure how the nickname 'Robin' crept into universal common

Robins are more at home among dense twiggy scrub than in high treetops or open country.

use in the British Isles! It seems to reflect the affection felt for these birds by so many of us who have encountered them in our gardens all through the year and experienced their engaging and confident behaviour. Elsewhere in Europe Robins are also widespread but they are relatively sparsely-distributed birds of woodland clearings and edges and do not generally associate with humans. Their high population density in Britain and Ireland probably reflects the unique mosaic pattern of our traditional countryside. Small fields, coppiced woods and hedgerows offered many straggly, dense, 'edge' habitats from which Robins could flit in and out of cover to feed along the margins of fields and tracks. Our traditional gardening style with hedges, shrubberies and lawns edged with herbacious cover offers similar habitat. It's no wonder Robins have adopted gardens as 'home from home', as farmland management departs from traditional methods.

The seasonal pattern is consistent but shows subtle between-years variations according to that year's winter weather and breeding success. The very sharp rise in late summer is probably the end of the moult, when youngsters are noisily expelled!

Many Robins migrate; those from north-eastern Scandinavia fly by night for 2,000 km or more and often stop to 'fill up' on the way in gardens near the east coast. Ringing has shown that most Robins in the British Isles are resident staying in more or less the same area all year round but short movements are common, depending on the weather. Gardens in newly-built housing estates may not offer enough resources for a pair to breed but might

Robin *Erithacus rubecula*

parts and breast are spotted with dark brown speckles and scallops until red breast starts to appear bit by bit in late summer. 'Plump' shape and 'perky', cocked head postures easy to recognise with practice. Short, low flits from perch to perch, ' tic, tic, tic' alarm call.

33

be adequate for a single bird to survive the winter, especially if food is provided. After the autumn moult when the speckled youngsters acquire their red breasts, they are driven away by their parents to seek their fortune elsewhere. Males bag most of the available vacant territories and a few young females will end up having to cross the Channel to survive their first winter. In the coldest weather even aggressive Robins forget about territory; this is the only time you will see groups of these otherwise antisocial birds feeding together in the garden.

Robins mostly eat insects, small worms and other soft foods, as you can tell from the thin bill (more like a Dunnocks's than a sparrow's) and only take hard vegetable matter such as peanuts in emergency, even then preferring small morsels. They really appreciate fat, a bird cake of salt-free dripping mixed with ground porridge oats and peanuts is ideal high-energy winter fuel. Many people tame Robins with mealworms but if cats are present it's not always good for them to become over-confident in the garden. They do not nest in holes, like tits, but insist on building an open nest which is often quite near the ground. This works well in a bramble thicket but is not so clever in a thornless garden shrub which cats can easily enter. The parent Robins risk their lives trying to drive attackers away but a young, agile cat will not leave their nest alone once well-grown young have revealed their presence by calling for food. Nests in sheds are often the most successful and best-protected, so leave a window open for them!

For some time, ornithologists were intrigued by suggestions that after fledglings left their nests their parents split them up, each parent only feeding certain individual youngsters. Actually proving this in a wild habitat is virtually impossible but Dr David Harper studied suburban Robins in the Cambridge University Botanical Garden and showed that it really does happen. The parent Robins chose to feed chicks of the opposite sex to themselves, a strategy that must be more efficient in some way because it only seemed to be adopted at times when food was less abundant. Gardens are very productive for behavioural research because the birds are easy to see and behave naturally, being accustomed to people.

Robins on the lawn often adopt this cocked head posture as if listening for worms. In fact they are probably using visual cues such as slight movements of the grass. Even at a distance, you can usually identify Robins by their familiar 'jizz', i.e. their shape, movements and postures.

'Constant Effort' ringing sites report large increases in Robins trapped, adults up by more than half since 1983, juveniles up by a quarter.

Male black with yellow bill, female brown. Simple? Actually many subtle plumage variations. Juveniles rufous-brown, mottled with buff streaks and feather edges especially throat and breast. After autumn moult, young males black but retain brown wing feathers, dark bill.

It surprises many people that such a widespread and apparently abundant garden bird should have been officially listed as a species of conservation concern but absolute scarcity is not the only criterion for such a listing. A large proportional decline in the total population is also a matter for concern and Blackbird numbers have in fact decreased significantly in the farmland and woodland habitats which used to support most of our birds. Increased numbers of Blackbirds seen in many gardens may be a reflection of a general shortage of resources for these birds. This

shows the importance of surveying bird numbers in as many different types of habitat as possible to be sure we are understanding the complete picture. Birds rapidly move from one type of habitat to another when times are hard and a rise in numbers seen in one type of habitat such as gardens does not necessarily therefore mean good news for the species.

Not all Blackbirds are black, this is a typical female, probably in its first winter. Older females can develop quite a lot of yellow on their bills. Juveniles of both sexes are also generally brown but a lot more streaky.

Blackbirds depend on soil invertebrates for food and on thick hedges or bushes for nesting. Gardens may nowadays provide more resources for them than much of the surrounding countryside. 'Improved' pasture and silage fields contain far fewer invertebrates than traditional meadows and traditional hedgerows continue to be destroyed or aggressively flailed.

Much of what we know about the lives and behaviour of Blackbirds has come from studying them in suburban gardens. Eric Simms studied their territorial behaviour in Dollis Hill, north London, for more than twenty-five years. He found that in this old-established residential area a pattern of surprisingly small territories

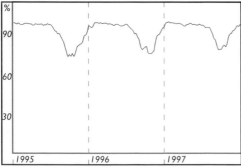

was remarkably stable around traditional breeding sites which were used almost every year by well-established dominant birds. If this habitat was of only marginal quality a more fluid pattern of occupation might be expected, younger birds struggling to get by in larger territories. On the contrary, it seems that Blackbirds are genuinely 'at home' in gardens, helped by their ability to nest in a wide variety of situations, unfussy acceptance of all kinds of bird table scraps in winter, relatively large size and

Blackbirds are seen in almost all gardens all year round, except in autumn when hedgerow fruits tempt some of them into the countryside and moulting birds tend to keep a low profile.

6,200,000 pairs. Blackbirds have been declining since the 1970s, by up to a third in some rural habitats. Population density varies greatly.

Blackbird *Turdus merula*

In spring, bill and eye ring yellow. Female bill dark, yellow base, but if bird survives more than one year, bill can become more yellow each year. Continental birds, in winter, often bigger with mottled plumage even in males. Fluty song, loud clanking alarm calls, especially at dusk.

35

determination to resist predators and their ability to forage effectively for food on lawns (assuming they are not drenched in worm-killing chemicals) which are not particularly productive for most other species. It remains to be seen how trends such as planting conifers and ground cover shrubs (rather than traditional hedges and beds with open soil for feeding) and building new housing estates with much smaller gardens will affect them.

BTO ecologist Dr Dan Chamberlain has compared the breeding success of Blackbirds in suburban gardens with those in a more 'natural' woodland habitat. Woodland nests suffered a high predation rate of around 80%, with corvids (Magpies, Jays, etc.) mainly responsible but wild mammals such as weasels also very active. In gardens the rate of predation was much lower at around 50%, which might be expected as there are generally fewer wild predators in inhabited areas, cats and Magpies being the main garden culprits.

The most significant problem in gardens seems to be that starvation of nestlings is more than twice as frequent as it is in woodland. Entire broods often succumb in warm dry weather when worms are hard to extract from lawns. In the woods there is a much greater variety of food, particularly caterpillars. Not only do fewer woodland nestlings starve, those that are not taken by predators tend to

Although birds will try anything when hungry, in general Blackbirds cannot hang from peanut feeders like tits. However they willl still benefit from peanuts in hard weather, so try to enable them to reach the nuts while discouraging competitors such as squirrels, not easy as they are about the same size! Notice the juvenile brown wing feathers, which show this bird is still in its first breeding year. Older males are uniformly black.

leave their nests in better condition than do garden fledglings. This probably increases their chances of surviving to breed the following year.

The implication for garden bird enthusiasts seems to be that increasing the variety and availability of invertebrates could help birds to breed more successfully as they are essential for the nestlings of virtually all garden species. This means reducing pesticide use to an absolute minimum and choosing native plants, upon which insects and their larvae can feed. However conifers, even aliens such as *leylandii,* do provide good concealed nesting sites. Many urban Blackbirds gamble by nesting in them very early, knowing they can try again if the first brood fails.

MEDIUM BTO ALERT   Found almost everywhere in the British Isles although sparse on uplands and windswept islands.

Less than 25 breeding pairs but probably increasing as European birds move nearer the coast. Average 750,000 winter visitors.

Apart from a tiny but increasing number of breeding pairs, Fieldfares cross the North Sea to visit us in winter. Sea Buckthorn berries revive incoming flocks which then move onto farmland, where they prefer to forage on worms and other invertebrates in open fields, particularly permanent pasture. If the soil is frozen they turn to fruit which they deplete in an intriguing order of preference, haws, then hips, then Ivy berries. Only in the hardest weather when fields are frozen and

hedges snowbound or already stripped will they resort to gardens where the food provided may save their lives.

Almost any berries are eaten when times are hard, including Yew, Rowan, Holly and even Cotoneaster but one way to attract them is to put out saved windfall apples, particularly after February when those in orchards have been exhausted. Although some late fruit may be taken from the trees,

Grey head contrasts with brown wings. Some show slight eyestripe. Flanks scalloped rather than spotted, no bold spots on belly unlike Mistle Thrush.

in general the birds perform a useful service to growers, clearing up damaged and rotting apples which might otherwise harbour pests and disease. Intensive farming destroys soil invertebrates, combined with unsympathetic management of hedgerows this could be making life harder for winter thrushes. Apples are low in protein with only a quarter as much as Rowan berries for example. It is debatable whether birds can survive on them for long, so berry-bearing garden trees and shrubs can really help.

Wintering populations are hard to monitor as the flocks are very mobile and anyway it is hard to tell how representative their numbers would be of the health of the breeding population. Certainly breeding Fieldfares are very productive.

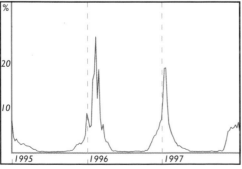

The exact timing of the winter peak depends on the weather and the natural food available.

They have to be, as with few humans around to interfere, natural populations of predators are still present in the northern forests and take about half the nestlings. To defend their nests Fieldfares breed in colonies. Research in Norway showed that smaller birds take advantage, building nests among the Fieldfares for protection. The whole structure of the forest bird community changes without Fieldfares; they seem to be a keystone species in this habitat.

Fieldfare Turdus pilaris

From larger Mistle Thrush by flash of orangey-buff under wing during fast, direct flight, shorter tail without obvious white edges, generally warmer brown colour, more musical song with many phrases repeated, more Blackbird-like 'chip, chip' alarm call, relatively timid.

37

The serious decline of the Song Thrush in woodland and farmland habitats has made it a headline bird of conservation concern. Research into the reasons for the decline continue, including post mortem analysis of corpses and detailed examination of life history data to try and find out where things are going wrong for this bird. Dr David Thomson and colleagues at the BTO have analysed details of the ringed birds found by members of the public. Their work suggests that nesting success has not changed and adult birds still seem to be living as long as ever. However a decrease in the survival of young birds in the first few weeks after leaving the nest appears to explain the overall population decline. This discovery should enable conservation bodies to target their resources on helping the vulnerable young birds and illustrates the value of collecting data over the bird's entire life cycle. As this species is very much at home in gardens, albeit slightly less confident than the larger Blackbird, looking after our young thrushes could really contribute to conserving them.

Song Thrush nests have a unique smooth mud lining. Nest Record Cards are very useful, but try not to draw the attention of predators.

With a shorter bill and slighter build than the Blackbird, Song Thrushes take a more limited range of prey than their bigger relative, extracting smaller worms from lawns and generally only from January to June whereas stronger Blackbirds can manage to pull them out of even quite dry summer grass. The smaller thrush often seems to lose out in any direct competition for food in gardens, although the two species successfully live side by side in many natural habitats, and is more fussy about nest sites. However there is one garden resource which only the Song Thrush seems to exploit efficiently, the snails which Blackbirds do not have the knack of opening and eating quickly. This suggests that in gardens with healthy snail populations, Song Thrushes have a food resource to fall back on even if Blackbirds monopolise the lawn and bird table. Blackbirds also tend to leave the fruits of Yew for their smaller cousin so, although slow-growing, female Yews are always a good choice for a bird garden.

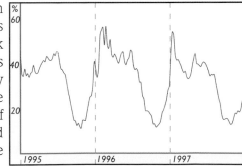

Marked seasonal cycle shows birds disappearing from gardens after breeding. The problem is, many young birds fail to reappear in winter.

Has declined by more than half, probably due to poor survival of juveniles. 1,380,000 pairs.

HIGH BTO ALERT

Turdus philomelos **Song Thrush**

38

Winter only. From slightly larger Song Thrush by stripey face (white supercilium and moustache, black eyestripe). Red flanks, grey-brown above, streaky white below. Gentle, shy, usually in twitchy flock, hungrily scoffs fruit, fussy, ignores seeds and scraps unless desperate.

Like the Fieldfare, Redwings are winter visitors. Because they come from pretty much the same places and for the same reason, if you see one of the two winter thrushes in a garden you are quite likely to see the other. Smaller and shorter-billed, Redwings are to Fieldfares as Song Thrushes are to Blackbirds, a bit shyer, a bit fussier about their food, a bit harder to help in a garden. Unlike other thrushes they seem reluctant to accept artificial foods, although sunflower hearts and mealworms would be worth testing in a hard winter. Generally they will only take fruit unless really starving; tried and tested thrush foods such as christmas pudding

literally leaving them cold although they may eventually resort to scraps when desperate. Planting berry-bearing bushes, particularly hawthorn, and providing apples are the best ways to help these shy, beautiful birds although they do tend to lose out in competition with both Starlings and their larger relatives so dispersing the apples around the garden is important.

Even in winter light, the bright, contrasting pattern of eyestripe and moustache on the side of the head easily identifies a Redwing.

Like all thrushes, when the ground is not frozen they really prefer animal food. Compared to Fieldfares they take smaller prey from the surface of the ground, shuffling through leaves more and digging less. Even the shy Redwing seems to come above the Song Thrush in the pecking order for winter food. This might suggest why the latter has been the first and fastest to decline among our native thrushes although in general, competition for food in thrushes does not seem as intense as it is among tits or finches.

Redwings usually migrate in the dark and if you hear soft 'tseep, tseep' calls

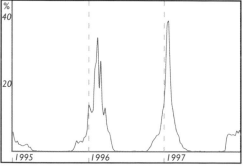

from above you on a crisp autumn night, a flock is probably passing overhead. In a rural garden with large shrubs or a thick, established hedge they may gather in the evening to roost, which can be quite a spectacular sight. Of all the thrushes they are the most erratic and unpredictable migrants, often visiting completely different parts of Europe in successive years. Birds ringed by BTO volunteers have been found in Italy and even Greece during subsequent winters.

Only cold midwinter weather brings shy Redwings into gardens, when fields are too frozen to probe for invertebrates and hedgerows exhausted.

Redwing *Turdus iliacus*

Largest thrush, upright, 'chesty', powerful bounding hops. From smaller Song Thrush by bright white underwing shown during undulating flight, 'rattle' alarm call, less musical song without repeats, white tail edges, bolder spots on belly, stands up to bullying Blackbirds!

39

The Mistle Thrush concerns many Garden BirdWatchers who worry that they are failing to distinguish it from the more familiar Song Thrush. 'Jizz' is all-important, Mistle Thrushes are bigger, greyer and more confident. They look bold and 'pigeon-chested', bouncing around the lawn like small Jays while Song Thrushes snoop around the border, a little wary. If all else fails, look for white feathers on the edge of the Mistle Thrush's tail, as it launches into its distinctive undulating flight, also showing bright white under the wings. Song Thrushes fly faster in a straight line, their underwings are a warm orange-brown although this is hard to see.

Generally a bird of larger gardens, the Mistle Thrush favours tall trees for both singing and nesting and often confirms its true identity with a characteristic rattling call when alarmed. Latest estimates suggest we have about four times as many Song Thrushes as Mistles, which seem to need much larger territories, rarely less than a hectare per pair and often more. Eric Simms found an average of 180 pairs of Blackbirds and 12 of Song Thrushes to each pair of Mistle Thrushes in his urban residential study area during the 1970s.

Bold, round spots on breast and belly and general grey tone suggest Mistle Thrush. Loud rattling calls, undulating flight and vigorous defence of its chosen berry bushes will confirm.

Like all our thrushes their diet is about half and half animal and vegetable, mostly animal in the breeding period then relying largely on fruit to sustain them through the autumn and winter. The name Mistle Thrush comes of course from Mistletoe and it has been suggested that the sparse distribution of the bird is linked to that of the berry but they seem to turn to Yew and Holly berries quite readily when Mistletoe is not available, albeit still taking far fewer types of berries and fruit than the very versatile Blackbird. Mistle Thrushes accept scraps and softer seeds in hard weather but their most characteristic habit is taking over a fruiting bush or tree and trying to defend it from all other birds, a noisy business!

Only about a quarter as many gardeners report Mistle Thrushes as report Song Thrushes

MEDIUM BTO ALERT Population decrease in farmland, although numbers seem stable in woodland. 320,000 pairs.

40

Sleek, streamlined, thin bill, male silvery grey with black cap. Female browner with brown cap. Stays within scrubby trees, hedges, flits or leaps intermittently pausing to sing in spring or eat berries in autumn. Often heard but not seen, distinctive song but in rural areas can

650,000 pairs. Population has been increasing steadily since the 1960s and range expanding northwards for unknown reasons.

Blackcaps are warblers, all of which have thin pointed bills unlike seed-eating sparrows and finches. By warbler standards the Blackcap's bill is relatively stout, reflecting its mixed diet which includes large quantities of fruit and berries in autumn and enabling wintering birds to make short work of peanuts. It is currently one of our most successful birds, which is a bit of a mystery as they favour mature deciduous woodland with a well-developed shrub layer, a habitat generally considered to be

under pressure from development, grazing or management changes. Tall trees are essential as songposts and hence most garden breeders are recorded in larger rural plots. Conifer plantations are disliked unless bordered with deciduous trees and the open, grazed woods of Wales and the west support very few of these birds.

Analysing nest record cards collected by BTO volunteers suggests that breeding performance has not really changed, so improved winter survival may be behind the population and range increases. One possible explanation is better enforcement of protection laws in their Mediterranean wintering areas enabling more Blackcaps to return unscathed each spring although

Males in their bright breeding plumage are easily observed, the loud song drawing attention. Later in the year they slip more unobtrusively through berry-bearing shrubs.

countless birds are still shot and trapped. Analysis of ringing recoveries estimated that as many as a quarter of west European Blackcaps may be killed by humans.

The domestic cat is probably the most important predator of our breeding Blackcaps, accounting for around ten percent of the ringed birds found each year. As Blackcaps will occupy more or less any suitable copse or scrap of woodland,

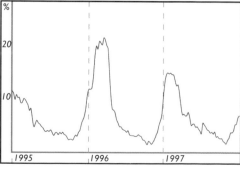

many of their nests are near homes and well within the prowling range of more than one cat so they are quite vulnerable. Of course, a problem with analysing causes of death from ringed birds is that only rings recovered by humans are included. Birds which starve, are taken by natural predators or fail to cross the sea successfully on migration are rarely found although a few rings can be retrieved from the nests of hawks and owls.

Rather surprisingly, in our gardens the Blackcap seems to be predominantly a winter visitor.

Blackcap *Sylvia atricapilla*

be confused with Garden Warbler which lacks black or brown cap. Slightly smaller than a sparrow. Wintering birds more visible, often take over peanut feeder, aggressive. Juveniles have brown caps, duller brownish wings. Males' caps progressively turn black in late summer.

41

Brambles are the preferred nest site so although near the ground the nests should be quite well-protected but extensive overgrown areas of bramble are now rare in many small woods so the birds have to make do with isolated clumps and shrubs. Elder, Hawthorn, wild Rose and tall thick clumps of Nettles are also used. Increasing range is only one of a number of changes in the ecology of this species which make the Blackcap well worth monitoring

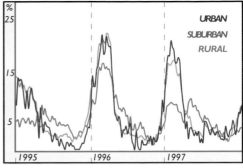

Site registration data analysis shows that winter Blackcaps prefer urban and suburban gardens to the rural plots favoured by summer visitors.

wherever it occurs. Dr C.F.Mason has shown that our summer visitors do seem to be arriving earlier in many areas than they did in the 1940s and 50s. Analysis of nest records by BTO ecologist Dr Humphrey Crick and colleagues has shown a trend towards earlier breeding which can be correlated with global climate change.

A very interesting discovery has come from studying our garden Blackcaps, most of which are seen in winter as can be seen from the reporting rate graph. Professor Peter Berthold's team in Germany suspected that some of their summer birds might be involved. By marking Blackcaps with lightweight coloured rings, so that individual birds could easily be recognised at garden feeders, it was found that our wintering birds were from a completely different population than our summer visitors which are still flying south for the winter as they always have done.

Experiments show that migration direction in Blackcaps is genetically controlled and inherited, hence subject to natural selection. West-European Blackcaps migrate south-west and eastern birds south-east but in central Europe there is a small intermediate population which migrates north-west and so tended not to survive. However in the last 40 years wintering conditions in Britain and Ireland seem to have improved, possibly helped by garden feeding, so instead of all these Blackcaps dying more and more of our wintering birds are surviving to breed the next spring and pass this unorthodox migration to their offspring. For higher animals such as birds it is very rare to be able to observe natural selection actually occurring in the wild during a human lifetime, so this is a remarkable study opportunity for everyone interested in evolution.

Female Blackcaps (and juveniles) have brown caps.

Common Birds Census records show an increase of over 50% in woodland and farmland study sites.

Very tiny, green, restless, constantly on the move, flicking wings, often detectd by thin, high calls. Wings and tail dark, black-edged crown bright orange in male, female's yellow. Juvenile like dull adult except no bright crown. Most likely in or around conifers.

The low garden reporting rate for our smallest bird belies its relative abundance in the countryside at large. When the whole of the British Isles was surveyed by volunteers between 1988 and 1991 for the most recent BTO/SOC/IWC atlas of breeding birds the population was found to be about the same as that of the Magpie with more than half a million pairs in Britain and an astonishing 300,000 or so in Ireland where it is very common, probably because of the milder winters. Being tiny and rarely using feeders, Goldcrests are hard to see and they also strongly prefer coniferous trees. Even if there is only one large conifer shared between

several suburban gardens a pair of Goldcrests will often be at home in it. They can be detected by their high-pitched calls as they travel a daily round, unobtrusively checking shrubs and compost heaps for insects.

In winter, numerous Goldcrests from northern Europe flood into eastern counties but most of our breeding Goldcrests more or less stay put all year round. Being so tiny, they are very vulnerable to cold weather, like Wrens and Long-tailed Tits. Much of their behaviour is therefore similar,

Although native conifers are more productive, Goldcrests will explore and even nest in Leylandii hedges. The tiny crest is not always obvious.

including roosting together in a huddle on cold nights (when they can lose up to 20% of their body weight) and building a warm, cosy pocket of a nest. Their nesting behaviour has been studied quite carefully and much learnt about how tiny creatures adapt to breed in climates that might seem far too cold for them. For example, to minimise heat loss Goldcrest

nestlings burrow to the lowest part of the snug hanging nest pocket once they have been fed, pushing hungry siblings to the top for their turn.

As you would expect, they are very productive to make up for high winter mortality. Females can start to lay a second clutch of 7-12 eggs (up to one and a half times her own weight) in another nest while her first brood of are still only half-grown. It's no wonder they seem to be constantly feeding.

Autumn and spring migration peaks show clearly but after a poor breeding season like 1996 Goldcrest numbers will be very low in gardens.

Goldcrest *Regulus regulus*

Very tiny body, long tail doubles overall length. Very small black bill. Unique colour combination, black, white and pink. Travel in groups, calling constantly, usually heard before seen. Regular 'beat', visiting gardens at same time every day. Juveniles duller, less pink, fluffy.

43

Another tiny bird with some intriguing adaptations to cold weather survival, the Long-tailed Tit has attracted considerable scientific attention as it seems to be one of the very few breeding birds in the British Isles which operate what is known as a 'cooperative breeding' system. Although in a different family from the true tits much of their behaviour in gardens is similar. However they never nest in holes (or nestboxes) but painstakingly construct fragile hanging pockets of cobwebs and feathers. Despite being intricately camouflaged with lichen these nests are very vulnerable to attack by Jays, Magpies and other predators. Only about half of them are successful. When a nest is destroyed, the adult birds do not try again but split up and do something quite fascinating, studied in detail by Dr Ben Hatchwell and others.

Hungry Long-tailed Tits are turning to peanuts, not the most obviously suitable food for their tiny, soft bills. Peanut flour and fat mixtures are ideal.

It seems that each bereaved parent teams up with a related male bird and his partner to help feed their nestlings and hence improve their condition and survival rate. Young Long-tailed Tits may end up being fed by four or even more adults, who are contributing to the propagation of their own genes as the young are all related to them. There is some evidence that adult birds which do not help at nests may be 'punished' by being forced to the outside of winter roosting 'huddles' which tend to consist of related birds and are vital for survival on the coldest nights. The discovery of cooperative breeding in a well-known garden bird is of great interest to science as this is a strategy more typical of tropical species.

The social nature of Long-tailed Tits is easily observed in gardens which they visit in noisy groups, often at quite regular times of the day. For the first time in many gardens they are starting to use peanut feeders, an odd choice of food for an almost entirely insectivorous bird, suggesting they may be short of natural resources. It will take time for any trend to show in the Garden BirdWatch reporting rates as numbers vary greatly each year depending on winter weather.

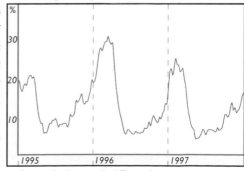

Generally, Long-tailed Tits only resort to garden feeders in late winter when natural food is scarce but they will breed in larger rural plots.

Populations fluctuate, probably due to winter weather, but general trend is positive and nesting productivity is increasing. 250,000 pairs.

Aegithalos caudatus **Long-tailed Tit**

From same-sized Blue and Coal tits by absence of blue or green, no white stripe down nape. Uniform brown above, light below, white cheeks. Glossy black cap, narrow black bib. Distinctive call, nasal 'pitchou, pitchou'. Usually some white on edges of bill, hard to see!

60,000 pairs. Woodland populations have declined by a third yet breeding has improved

MEDIUM BTO ALERT

The problem with monitoring Marsh and Willow Tits is that they are very difficult to tell apart unless their songs or calls are heard. Because of this they are recorded together in Garden BirdWatch, a shame because there are some interesting ecological differences between the two which might be well illustrated by their use of different gardens. One thing both have in common is that they are clearly declining in Britain (neither is present in Ireland). The reasons are rather obscure, although probably linked to habitat problems. Marsh Tits are among the most sedentary of

birds, they seem to pair for life and stick to their territory which is quite large by tit standards, averaging about 2.5 hectares. They sometimes enlarge nesting holes but never excavate a new one from scratch, insisting on recycling existing cavities.

This could be one reason why they are strongly associated with large mature deciduous trees. Nestboxes are used if they are placed appropriately within a territory but the chances of this are always low. It is worth mounting a couple of extra tit boxes on mature trees at head height or even lower if Marsh Tits are regularly seen in your garden.

Narrow black bib and white cutting edges on bill are typical of Marsh Tit but these do vary and are not always easy to see.

You may need half a dozen or more as the local Blue Tits will need to be accommodated first before the Marsh Tits get a look in.

Like Coal Tits, Marsh Tits are great hoarders. Much has been learnt about how and why animals find and retrieve stored food by studying them. An Oxford University team labelled sunflower seeds with tiny amounts of short-lived radioactivity. Those hidden by Marsh Tits were located with a geiger counter. The

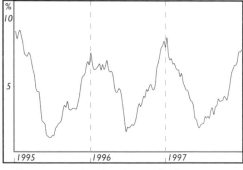

Clear seasonal cycles despite the low reporting rate demonstrate the accuracy of our data.

birds hid seeds for a short time, generally a day or less, rather than cacheing them away for the winter. This suggests that they hide any food they come across not as a long-term store but because it would be monopolised by dominant birds such as Great Tits were they to discover it as well. Individual Marsh Tits specialised in particular hiding places such as grass, moss or leaves but periodically changed preferences, perhaps when their seeds were being discovered too easily.

Marsh Tit Parus palustris

From almost identical Marsh Tit only reliably by song and call, Willow Tit never says 'pitchou'. Otherwise, wing feathers in spring less uniform brown, some pale edges, black bib wider, less neat, black cap dull rather than glossy, bill all black, cheeks whiter. Not easy!

45

This species was not recognised in Britain until 1897 when visiting German ornithologists noticed that two skins in the British Museum labelled 'Marsh Tit' looked more like their continental Willow Tits. Another fifty years of confusion followed when our birds were mistakenly considered to be the same species as the American Black-capped Chickadee, which illustrates how hard it is to separate these brown tits. It is also hard to guess whether Marsh or Willow Tits might be the commoner in gardens. Because both have large territories it probably depends more than anything else on the type of woodland surrounding the bigger rural plots which they are most likely to visit. Willow Tits are associated with conifers, higher altitudes, birch trees (in which they often excavate their nest holes) and as the name implies, Willows and Alder carr along the damp margins of rivers, streams and gravel pits. Confusingly, the Marsh Tit prefers drier habitats! A bird seen in conifers is almost certainly a Willow Tit, as Marsh Tits like broad-leaved woods and hence are almost entirely absent from Scotland apart from the eastern borders, whereas there are quite a few scattered Willow Tits across to Galloway and around the Clyde. It would be fascinating but difficult to study these preferences in gardens.

Because our Marsh and Willow Tits are so sedentary, if you have them in the garden at all you should notice them year after year. Garden records of such predictable species are therefore very precious in monitoring your local environment. If they disappear, this suggests that something pretty drastic has happened to the woodlands in your area, especially as Willow Tits are very hardy little birds. They have a more northern distribution than the Marsh Tit and on cold nights can reduce their metabolic rate and body temperature to survive, taking quite a long time to wake up in the morning. In Siberia they dig roosting tunnels in the snow!

Willow Tits insist on excavating a new nesting hole each season so nestboxes must be stuffed with polystyrene or wood shavings to interest them and should be mounted quite low in thick cover. Their nests can be told from those of Marsh Tits by the absence of any moss. Help with coppicing on a local nature reserve and you might acquire some Silver Birch logs. When these start to soften a bit, attach a few to your own trees. If Willow Tits are in the area they may dig holes and nest in them.

Willow Tits in fresh plumage can sometimes be told from Marsh Tits by the pale edges to their wing feathers, unfortunately these wear off rapidly as nesting progresses.

Parus montanus **Willow Tit**

From similar-sized Blue Tit by white stripe down nape, absence of sky blue. Head black and white, breast and belly white, flanks variably buff. Juveniles dull, look much greener but distinctive nape strip already present. Not as sociable as other tits. Two note 'peechoo' song.

900,000 pairs. Not as badly affected by cold winters as other small birds, Coal Tits have increased by more than 50% in some woodlands.

Coal Tits discover black sunflower seeds incredibly quickly when they are first provided in a garden, often investigating a new feeder within a minute or two of installation and hiding away seed after seed in places they do not always remember. Faced with an abundance of food, they fussily reject seeds which are not quite the right size for them, gratefully received by the Chaffinches below or, more irritatingly, germinating into a sunflower lawn! Particularly at home in coniferous woods, their

relatively slender beaks are better at extracting food from clusters of pine needles than those of other tits.

Blue and Great Tits will exclude Coal Tits from nesting sites so this more timid bird often uses holes too small for the other species to squeeze into. Try

Lack of blue eliminates Blue Tit, lack of yellow and small size eliminates Great Tit. Wide black bib eliminates Marsh Tit so the Coal Tit on the left could only be confused with Willow Tit. When it turns round, the diagnostic white nape is clear.

boxes with holes as tight as 24 mm or small vertical slit entrances and, if you have conifers, mount the boxes

very low on their trunks, considering the presence or absence of cats. Or saturate your garden with boxes every few yards. Blue and Great Tits only nest within minimum distances of each other, leaving boxes inbetween vacant for Coal Tits.

Because of their convenient habit of using nestboxes, the whole life cycle of the Coal Tit is relatively easy to study and this means that the impact of environmental changes on these birds can be more completely understood. An example of this type of research took place when insecticides sprayed from the air were first used

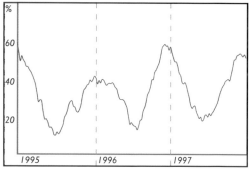

Three years' records are not really enough to be sure whether the apparent upward trend is real but other BTO surveys confirm that Coal Tit numbers seem to be increasing slowly.

in Scottish pine plantations to control the Pine Beauty moth, a serious pest. Coal Tit nestboxes were installed in the sprayed forests and the breeding performance of the birds carefully monitored. No obvious short-term effects were found but it is also important that any long-term trends are spotted. At the moment, the Coal Tit population seems to be increasing. This suggests that although the ecosystem of commercial pine plantations is limited, at least it is not deteriorating.

Coal Tit *Parus ater*

Sky blue crown and wing feathers, blue tail. Underparts yellow, face white 'bridled' dark blue. Juveniles much duller, yellow, green and dark grey, from young Coal Tit by absence of lighter stripe on nape. More agile than heavier Great Tit, acrobatic, churring alarm calls.

With a garden reporting rate of nearly a hundred percent in winter this very abundant and still increasing species would be most people's first thought if asked to mention a typical garden bird. Naturally a bird of deciduous woods, Blue Tits tend to select nestboxes attached to Oaks rather than other species of tree. Oaks support huge numbers of invertebrates, particularly the caterpillars on which the birds can rear their enormous broods of ten or even more nestlings. Continental Blue Tits are often winter visitors to south-eastern counties where some stay to breed, producing larger and brighter offspring than our resident race. Bird ringers will tell you that if you put a mist net up on the Moon you would probably catch a Blue Tit but in fact this bird has a smaller range than Coal or Great Tits, being replaced east of Moscow by the Azure Tit and to the north by the Siberian Tit. This is an example of how bird species with similar food and habitat requirements can avoid competition by remaining geographically separate.

The juvenile on the left will lack the bright sky blues of an adult until late summer.

Professor Christopher Perrins and his team at Oxford University have studied tits in nestboxes for many years and discovered a great deal of fundamental information about the biology of birds from these common species. Different tit species each occupy their own ecological niche. Coal Tits will often nest on the only conifer in a mixed wood, whereas Blue Tits will choose to nest in a clump of birches within a pine plantation. The average size of insects taken by each species is different as are the average heights at which they feed. In winter Blue Tits in woods forage mostly among twigs but Great Tits often feed on the ground. In the hard winter of 1962-3 many Great Tits died in thick snow but Blue Tits survived in the trees above. When birds share garden feeders this specialisation breaks down and competition comes down to aggression, strength and established dominance hierarchies within the local population. Brave and agile, Blue Tits can usually grab at least a share of any available food!

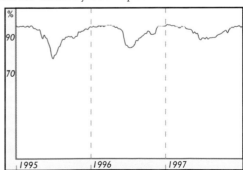

There's hardly a garden without a Blue Tit and the graph seems to be flattening as more gardens keep their birds all through the year. This might well be linked to increasing summer feeding.

Very abundant species with stable and even slightly increasing population, helped through winters by garden feeding. 4,400,000 pairs.

Parus caeruleus **Blue Tit**

Black and white head, bright yellow breast with black stripe running down centre which is thinner in female. No sky blue or white stripe down nape. Largest tit, chunky, slightly less agile than Blue Tit. Breeding adults glossy, bright. Juveniles look washed-out, dull, less contrast.

The Great Tit population increased noticeably in the late 1970s but since then has fluctuated about a more or less steady level.

Probably the most studied bird species in the world, the Great Tit still has secrets but long-term research programmes have revealed a much greater flexibility, variety of survival strategies and what can only be described as 'intelligence' than would have been thought possible in any bird fifty years ago. Flexibility is a key to success in the wild and Great Tits have a very wide distribution as a result, present throughout Europe, North Africa and much of Asia including the tropics and Japan. Intensely social, Great Tits are almost constantly interacting with each other not

least through their more or less continuous calling and wide repertoire of loud songs. In deciduous woods during early spring, any song you cannot recognise is most likely to be a Great Tit although the piercing, persistent 'dee-choo, dee-choo' is their most common refrain. Very irritating it is too, if performed outside the bedroom window early in the morning!

Our largest tit has some blue fringes on wing feathers but never the bright sky blue of a Blue Tit. Green, yellow and black dominate.

One of the main reasons for this constant communication is that the birds maintain a dominance hierarchy in which birds at the top of the 'pecking order' have preferential access to food. This hierarchy is continually being challenged, especially in winter when the flocks of Great Tits that form in the autumn often aggregate together at food resources such as Beech mast or in gardens with many feeders. The black stripe down the yellow breast plays a key role as it seems to be a badge of good physical condition: dominant birds tend to have larger black stripes. A female's peters out halfway down her belly

whereas the males' are bold and black right down between the legs.

Many people wonder whether the appearances and characters of animals (and people) are inherited or determined by their environment. A great advantage of the Great Tit as a study species is that it nests in boxes and tolerates quite intrusive experiments that could never be performed on more sensitive species. 'Brood manipulations' when chicks are swapped between parents can be carefully performed (under licence) to

Lower reporting rate than Blue Tit reflects lower population, and possibly the fact that the holes in most commercial nest boxes are too small!

Intelligent and inquisitive, often first species to investigate new garden feeding devices. Calls similar to Blue Tit but distinctive two note song in spring. Typical tit bill shape, intermediate between triangular seed-eaters' (e.g. Greenfinch) and pointed insectivores' (e.g. Dunnock) bills.

49

examine how much of the characteristics of the offspring are due to inherited genes ('nature') and how much to parenting and environment ('nurture'). As far as size is concerned it seems that the nature/nurture balance depends on the food supply. When food is abundant, all the youngsters in the population attain their full genetic potential so larger birds rearing their own chicks raise the largest young by inheritance. When food is short all chicks are generally smaller but the larger birds can still raise the largest young even if they are given the chicks of smaller adults; not directly due to inheritance but simply because they are able to grab more food.

So size is clearly important for Great Tit survival and we might therefore ask why they do not keep getting bigger every year. The wild environment is so variable that conditions could suddenly change at any time to favour smaller birds, for example in a disastrous beech mast season lighter birds that could feed on the slender twigs of silver birch, for example, might survive better than larger, less agile individuals. Also, the range of viable sizes is constrained by the available ecological niche. If they grew gradually bigger they would have to start competing with Starlings for larger prey. Any really tiny Great Tits would be excluded from food by Blue Tits as well as their bigger relatives. So we would expect a population of Great Tits to include birds of different sizes within a narrow range.

Dr Andy Gosler has investigated one of their most intriguing strategies. It might seem reasonable to assume that dominant birds would be the heaviest but for Oxfordshire Great Tits in winter this is no longer true. Now, birds at the top of the pecking order seem to be staying slim.

Breeding birds have glossy caps. The width of the black stripe indicates physical condition and dominance, it is narrower in females.

Trim figures are in fashion with Great Tits as fatter birds are more vulnerable to Sparrowhawks. When hawks returned to Oxfordshire as their numbers recovered from pesticide poisoning dominant Great Tits, which had previously carried the most fat, lost weight! They could grab any available food whenever it suited them, so there was no need to carry a 'spare tyre'. Subordinate birds, on the other hand, still have to carry fat reserves because they may be excluded from limited food supplies when times are hard. This kind of amazing flexibility helps to explain why despite the return of the Sparrowhawks, the population of Great Tits has not declined.

Over the last 25 years, population has increased by about a quarter. Found throughout British Isles except upland and fens. **2,000,000 pairs.**

Parus major **Great Tit**

130,000 pairs. Population increasing and range expanding northwards. Larger broods and earlier laying may be linked to climate change.

Always exciting when it suddenly appears and assertively takes possession of a peanut feeder, the woodpecker-like jizz and exotic plumage make Nuthatches fairly easy to recognise. Nonetheless, because of their sparse distribution they are not familiar to many gardeners. Every year the BTO receives a few claims of incredible rarities which turn out to be Nuthatches! A small but chunky pointed creature scuttling down and around a tree trunk head first can only be this bird, unless you are in Ireland or most of Scotland, where Nuthatches do not occur. A loud and distinctive call is usually the first sign that one is on its way to your feeders.

Nuthatches can feed comfortably at any angle, including upside down.

A few birds have started to breed in southern Scotland as part of a slow range expansion but in general Nuthatches are extraordinarily sedentary, making only short flights from tree to tree. Even when young continental birds must move some distance to find winter food they almost never cross the sea as far as anybody knows. Although some birds are moving into new areas, many gardeners report that they have lost their Nuthatches in recent years, probably linked to the removal or pruning of a mature tree in the area. They will use nextboxes, plastering round the hole with mud until it meets an exact specification, which only they seem to know! Try providing several boxes with holes of different sizes. A Nuthatch's nest illustrates the diversity of resources required if wild birds are to thrive. They prefer old holes in large, mature deciduous trees but like to line them with bark flakes from conifers, expecially Scots Pine. So just to nest they need a big broad-leaved tree, a big conifer and a supply of wet mud, all within a territory they are very reluctant to stray out of.

The Nuthatch reporting rate is fairly low but increases in a colder winter. As their range expands we might expect a slight upward trend.

Nuthatches operate in pairs throughout the year but otherwise are extremely antisocial. Even fledglings cannot tolerate each other's company so you will never see them feeding together in a group like young tits. Pairs defend their territories violently, partly because each contains large caches of food to see them through the winter.

Nuthatch Sitta europaea

Streaky brown above, pale below, thin downcurved bill. Blue Tit size but looks slimmer. Shy, mousy tree trunk climber, undulating flight from tree to tree with thin, quiet 'tsee' call. Works up and around tree bottom to top, then repeats on next tree. Sexes and juveniles similar.

51

Treecreepers creep on trees, although they sometimes risk a little creep up an old wall and may even nest in old sheds or woodpiles. And they do fly, of course, but only to the next tree although Treecreepers in the far north of Norway are forced to migrate in winter. Mouse-like behaviour is matched by a squeaky high-pitched call often heard from an invisible bird well-camouflaged on a matching brown background. Less often recognised is their thin but surprisingly musical short song, ending with a confident flourish.

Rural gardeners with mature trees are most likely to see Treecreepers. *Wellingtonia* is a favourite for roosting, look for white droppings on the trunk. Sometimes Treecreepers join winter tit flocks but generally they are very sedentary. This saves us an identification problem as just over the Channel lives a virtually identical but distinct species, the Short-toed Treecreeper *Certhia brachydactyla.* Don't worry about this unless you live in the Channel Islands!

Research in Finland showed that the number of eggs laid depends on day length which is very hard to demonstrate in other birds because variable weather and food supplies obscure the pattern. This result is interesting as it suggests that tree trunks are a relatively stable, predictable 'microenvironment' in which the density of food is fairly constant. If this is true, then the evolution of two very similar Treecreeper species makes

When the white belly is pressed against the trunk, the bird is almost invisible, as is the characteristic thin, downcurved beak when full of food!

more sense. In predictable environments such as tropical forests, many similar species can evolve into very narrow, specialised ecological niches. Where resources are less predictable, we tend to find fewer species which are more versatile.

Such a specialist bird may seem beyond help in a garden, but try importing assistance into their arboreal environment rather than expecting them to emerge from it. Fat smeared on tree trunks and peanuts wedged into the bark will be taken in winter. Small nesting pockets are readily used if attached to the trunk about three metres up.

Secretive, especially in the breeding season.

Population stable, limited by large territories but may increase as conifer plantations mature. Breeding performance improving. 250,000 pairs.

Certhia familiaris **Treecreeper**

Exotically-coloured crow, mostly brownish-pink with white rump and vent, black tail. Wings black and white, flashed with bright blue. White chin, black moustache, paler below. Streaky crown feathers can be raised into a 'crest'. Intelligent, quite wary, 'bounces' along ground

170,000 pairs. Overall, our Jay population seems fairly stable but numbers in farmland have dropped worryingly, by about a third.

Jays are quick and agile among trees but look a bit troubled by longer flights. This, and the relatively low garden reporting rate, reflect their favoured deciduous woodland habitat and sedentary nature although continental birds will move rapidly if food is short, quite often reaching south-eastern England in a difficult winter. Wherever there are Oaks you will find Jays, from Ireland right across Asia, but in our treeless northern isles they are definitely a 'twitch'. They have a specially enlarged

oesophagus lubricated with copious saliva for transporting many acorns which they hide in small holes in the ground.

In autumn each single Jay can collect and hoard as many as 2,000 acorns as well as hazel nuts and beech mast, burying them where they are safe from other consumers. They retrieve most of them but a few are left to germinate. Although most woods are managed by humans these days, Jays are the most important natural planters of

A quite large, exotically-coloured bird in the garden is always exciting, even if it's only come to peck holes in your apples!

Oaks. They may take eggs and nestlings but they do renew the songbirds' habitat.

The unusual colouring, particularly the bright metallic blue on the wings, gives Jays a rather exotic look and gardeners are often quite pleased to see them. In fact Jays are just as keen to raid songbird nests as their vilified cousin the Magpie. Being a little smaller, they are more easily repulsed by the Blackbirds but they often work in pairs, one Jay nipping into the nest while its owner is distracted by another.

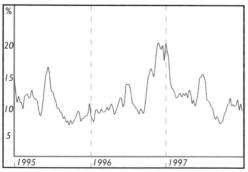

The Jay's amazing learning ability and memory have been well-studied thanks to the ease with which they adapt to captivity. Some gardeners are captivated by these colourful characters and hand-feed Jays extravagantly with anything from mealworms to pecans although they are quite happy with peanuts. A benefit of their presence in an organic garden (if you can keep them off your peas!) is that apart from the Song Thrush they are the only garden bird that eats significant numbers of snails.

Wary Jays are spotted in relatively few gardens but there is a definite peak in the nesting season and they become more visible in a cold winter.

Jay *Garrulus glandarius*

Appears black and white from a distance but in fact has iridescent sheens on wings and tail. Flies like a battered kite, rising awkwardly with mixture of quick flaps and glides but determined and agile among trees. Sidles or kangaroo-hops along ground with tail held high.

53

The Magpie is just as intelligent and versatile as the Jay and a little larger and more powerful than its more colourful relative. Both these members of the crow family share a wide range of feeding behaviours. However each bird must specialise enough so that each has its own ecological niche, from which the other species will not entirely exclude it when times are hard. While Jays favour mature broad-leaved woodland, Magpies are more at home in open country, farmland, scrub, parks and gardens, feeding on the ground much more confidently. Just as the Song Thrush resorts to snails when excluded by larger Blackbirds from other food, Jays have their hidden acorns which Magpies do not seem to hoard in the same way. Intriguingly, most Magpie caches are of perishable items, which they return to within a week or so rather than relying on them as a long-term investment.

Two for joy? Young Magpies have short tails and lack the iridescent blues and greens of the adults.

Grain has traditionally been very important for Magpies in autumn, but this could be changing as cereal harvests become earlier and stubble fields fewer although Magpies have been quick to exploit trends such as free-range pig rearing in open fields. Magpie numbers have increased greatly and they are certainly moving into suburban and even urban areas where they can find plenty of easily-accessible carrion and refuse to feed on through the winter, often a difficult time for crows in the countryside. Urban Magpies enter the breeding season in good condition, to boost the diets of their own youngsters with the seasonal luxury of songbird eggs and nestlings. The limited number of suitable sites for their very large nests may limit further increases in town breeders.

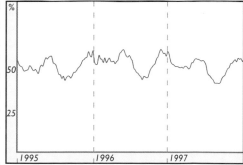

About half of us report Magpies in gardens, with peaks in winter and the nesting season. In summer some birds forage on farmland but the reporting rate is remarkably constant overall.

Research is underway at the BTO to monitor Magpie numbers. If their nest predation is really to blame for songbird declines, as some people persistently claim in letters to newspapers and

Population has roughly doubled since the early 1970s but since the late 1980s numbers have been fairly stable in rural habitats. *1,000,000 pairs.*

Nesting productivity has greatly increased, average laying date nearly three weeks earlier. May be due to climate or move into suburbs.

elsewhere, this should show up in our volunteers' data in several different ways.

At the simplest level, obvious ecological relationships between species whose numbers are changing can be critically examined. If we hypothesise that nest predation by Magpies causes songbird numbers to decline because more eggs and young are destroyed, then it is surprising that one of the species which has declined the most, according to BTO volunteers' data, is the Tree Sparrow. This bird nests in holes and its nestlings are relatively safe from Magpies, so it cannot really be true that Magpies are responsible for all songbird declines.

For a more sophisticated analysis, we need long-term data, monitoring the process which we suspect is being affected, in this case songbird nesting. Magpies prey mostly on eggs and nestlings and luckily the nest record cards completed by BTO volunteers provide a great deal of data on the success rates of nesting songbirds over a long period of time. This information is vital if we are to understand the causes of change in bird populations. For a number of declining songbirds including the Song Thrush, nest records show us that breeding success has not really changed, so nest predation cannot have caused their declines. The average number of fledglings leaving each nest has not changed enough, across the country as a whole, to account for the observed drop in the number of adults.

Given enough data, even more refined methods using advanced statistical techniques can be used to investigate whether trends in Magpie numbers match the trends in songbird numbers. To do this, reliable survey data over a long enough

period to show genuine population trends rather than short-term fluctuations are needed and again we are lucky to have such data, provided by BTO volunteers. Increases in Magpies should have happened in the same places and over the same time scales as declines in their prey species, if Magpies have in fact caused the songbird declines. No such correlations have been found in the survey data, suggesting that general Magpie increases and general songbird declines in the countryside are due to independent coincidental causes.

This does not of course mean that Magpies are not a problem for songbirds in some localised areas and they are probably the second most important predator in many gardens after the domestic cat. However due to the absence of wild mammals such as weasels, many suburban garden birds probably still suffer less predation than they would experience in natural woodlands and farmland hedgerows.

Magpie *Pica pica*

Small crow, compact, size of a pigeon, short bill. Grey nape contrasts with black cap and bib, otherwise dark except for obvious pale eye. Stylish, confident, sociable, aerobatic. Conversational, noisy, calls more modulated and resonant than other crows. Juveniles a bit duller.

55

Grey on the back of the head and a pale eye distinguish Jackdaws although at a distance they can be mistaken for other black crows, so compare sizes. Jackdaws are the smallest crows in Europe, only three quarters the size of a Carrion Crow. They bustle about actively and rather warily on the ground and, unlike Jays, are confident and acrobatic flyers. Jackdaws string together their eerie, resonant calls into an almost musical 'song' by crow standards, reminiscent of the wild cliffs and spooky ruins on which they nest. They are equally at home in large gardens and readily use nest boxes although they prefer privacy. Try hiding boxes behind chimney stacks, rather than hanging them in full view. This might persuade them not to nest in your chimney! The same nest is used every year; entomologists have studied their insect communities and found that an amazing diversity of fauna builds up, including fifty different species of beetle.

Grey plumage not always easy to see if the birds are moving quickly but small size, calls and agile, flighty behaviour suggest Jackdaw. Pale eye of adult confirms.

Like Rooks, Jackdaws are gregarious and sociable. Pairs stay together for life, which can be five years or longer, gathering together to feed and roost in flocks outside the breeding season. Young Jackdaws' eyes are blue, changing to brown for their first winter and the pearly white of an adult as they come into breeding condition. They visit more gardens than most people realise, warily sneaking in just after dawn while we are still asleep. They will take anything left on the bird table and even hang from feeders although their stubby bill restricts what they can extract.

BTO ecologist Dr Ian Henderson showed that it is surprisingly difficult for a pair of Jackdaws to find enough food to raise their entire brood. Although both male and female work hard, many chicks starve. The huge effort required is reflected in an early summer peak in the garden reporting rate and explains why the pair bond is so strong. Just a single brood is attempted and the pair simply give up for that year if they fail. This strategy works for a long-lived species as they can try again the next season.

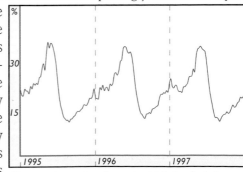

The garden reporting rate plot for Jackdaws shows an extraordinarily regular seasonal cycle.

Farmland population has roughly doubled in the last 25 years with improved breeding performance but now seems steady. **600,000 pairs.**

Corvus monedula **Jackdaw**

From all black Carrion Crow by white bare skin at base of bill and shape of head (with practice - forehead seems higher and bill more pointed). Juveniles black-faced but all ages have 'baggy trousers', shaggy feathers at tops of legs. Very sociable, rarely seen alone.

Most Rook records are from larger gardens near farmland, as might be expected for a bird so closely associated with agriculture and with large mature trees. They are more specialised feeders than other crows and less widely distributed, being largely absent from Scandinavia and Siberia, for example, where Carrion or Hooded Crows abound. Their diet has been intensively studied because of their perceived importance as an agricultural pest, by Professor Chris Feare and others. The most important foods are grain and soil invertebrates, particularly earthworms the availability of which probably limits their nesting season.

Rooks are best known for their nests, in dramatically large, noisy and visible treetop colonies. Successful pairs stay together for several years, often for life, and the male is a dedicated provider. For about two weeks he has to feed the incubating female as well as himself, then for the first couple of weeks after the eggs have

hatched he feeds the entire family, flying constantly between the rookery and the nearest grassland where earthworms can be found. This can be some distance away, especially in an area of intensive arable farming which greatly reduces soil invertebrate populations. If the weather is too cold or too dry he may starve.

With practice, Rooks can be recognised even at a distance. Large black birds in a big flock like this will almost always be Rooks as Carrion Crows are much less sociable and Jackdaws much smaller. If in doubt listen for their distinctive calls.

Late summer is even harder for Rooks as earthworms retreat deep into the soil, and the birds need about twenty percent more energy to replace their moulting feathers. Many of the youngsters die. In colder weather Rooks turn to vegetable food and this is when the conflict arises. Grain, peas, beet and potato seed may all

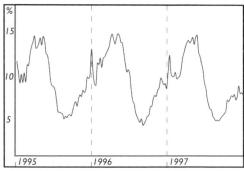

be removed from fields. More efficient harvesting and the disappearance of stubbles means that Rooks must resort to drilled seed in autumn and perhaps animal feeds in winter. Yet they do seem to be holding on and even increasing their numbers somewhat. In other countries Red Kites and Goshawks kill many of the Rooks and Jackdaws of which farmers complain yet both these magnificent raptors were persecuted to the edge of extinction in the British Isles.

Similar seasonal cycle to Jackdaw but with a small, intriguing winter peak at New Year.

Rook *Corvus frugilegus*

From Rook by black face and simple, no-nonsense call, flatter crown, slightly heavier bill, 'underpants' rather than 'trousers'. Antisocial, usually alone or in small family party. In Northern Scotland and Ireland, pied grey and black Hooded Crow is a race of the same species.

57

The two distinctive plumages of this species are a fascinating example of how living creatures change their appearances and distributions over evolutionary time. Black crows of the race *Corvus corone corone* are found in western Europe, including England, Wales and south-eastern Scotland. In eastern Asia *Corvus corone orientalis* is also black, but in between these two isolated populations of similar birds we find the grey and black Hooded Crow *Corvus corone cornix* which also inhabits Ireland and north-western Scotland. The three races of crow probably evolved in isolation during the last ice age, then as the ice retreated they all met up again. Races of the same species which are in contact of enormous scientific interest as they may tell us a lot about how new species evolve.

Where two races interbreed a 'hybrid zone' arises in which we find individuals with the characteristics of both races. This has certainly happened with crows. Carrion and Hooded Crows interbreed freely but the hybrid zone is stable, quite narrow and hybrids almost never occur outside it. Natural selection works against each race if it moves to the 'wrong' side of the zone,

Large, dark-eyed, quiet crow with no white skin at the base of its black, dagger-like beak. Alone or in small family group. Juvenile Rooks also lack white face but are usually in a noisy flock.

in general Carrion Crows doing better in lowland and wooded habitats, Hooded Crows in open or upland habitats. A stable hybrid zone that does not widen implies that the hybrids are inferior in some way to either of the pure races, otherwise the birds would interbreed freely until all were hybrids and the distinct races disappeared.

A theory called 'speciation by reinforcement' predicts that if this is the case, the genes of birds which never hybridise will be favoured by natural selection and hence the two races will slowly diverge into two different species. Computer simulations show that this is possible but like many theories about the actual mechanisms of evolution it remains debatable. In fact the hybrid zone is moving north, leaving more Carrion Crows and fewer Hoodies in the British Isles. This reduction in our biodiversity could be linked to global warming

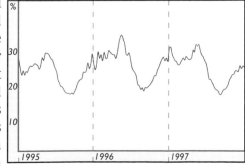

Garden reporting rate is surprisingly high at about twenty-five percent year-round.

Steadily increasing, populations in woodland have roughly doubled since 1971 possibly due to decline in gamekeeping. 1,300,000 pairs.

Smaller, more upright and short-tailed than Blackbird, walking not hopping, quarrelsome, adventurous, agile, noisy. Very versatile, hangs from branches and feeders, probes ground, catches flying insects. Base of yellow bill in breeding season is blue for a boy, pink for a girl.

When large flocks of Starlings visit gardens in cold weather the noise and consumption of food can be enough to put anybody off a bird, but this is becoming a rare event in most areas as this species seems to be declining significantly, so perhaps we should welcome Starlings rather than take them for granted. It is certainly worth putting up some large nest boxes with 45 mm entrance holes, especially on new estates with Starling-proof eaves. Starlings are a very sociable species, feeding and roosting in loose flocks full of comings and goings and constant noisy squabbling. Even

when plenty of food is provided and fighting seems a waste of energy, they still quarrel and many people wonder why they bother. Maintaining a dominance hierarchy or 'pecking order' may not affect access to a well-stocked bird table but it is of vital importance to the birds when other resources are limited and so knowing which bird is boss could make all the difference at other times of year.

Sexing Starlings is quite easy and fun. Males have entirely dark eyes but most females have a brown ring round the edge. In the breeding season, their beaks turn yellow, those of males are pale blue at the base so this bird is a female.

The resources used by Starlings have been well studied, by Professor Chris Feare and others, because their food consumption is of economic importance to farmers and their droppings are a nuisance in many cities although less so now that there are fewer large urban roosts. Although they feed in

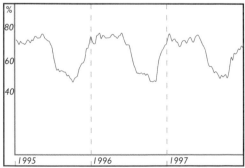

Many Starlings still prefer farmland in late summer, it will be important to monitor this.

flocks all year round, from the end of January each male must defend a small territory immediately around his chosen nest site. Dominant males try to defend several sites but the less suitable holes are pinched one by one, while they are busy attracting a mate by singing and decorating a nest with petals or leaves.

Dominance is important during nesting as males must guard their mates carefully against the attentions of other males. Polygyny (males fertilising the

Starling Sturnus vulgaris

Juveniles plain mid-brown, dark dagger-like bill, strong legs and feet, look quite strange when moulting into dark, spotty adult plumage. Both sexes spotty in winter, bill turns brown. Vast repertoire of calls, whistles, bubbling songs and mimicry. Fast flight on pointed wings.

59

eggs of more than one female) is common, as are other intriguing behaviours such as nest parasitism (laying eggs in other Starlings' nests) and the removal and dumping of eggs from other neighbouring Starlings' nests.

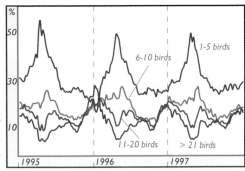

In late summer a hierarchy of feeding methods can be seen among Starlings. Grassland is the favourite feeding habitat and this tends to be monopolised by the adults while the juveniles feed in trees. Dominance is still probably involved but things are not always as simple as they

Garden BirdWatch flock size records show how large flocks are seen in winter, small groups in the breeding season, as we would expect.

seem. Juvenile Starlings' skulls are weaker than those of adults and they probably cannot perform the characteristic open-billed probing into the ground so strongly and efficiently. In fact mortality among young Starlings is rather high, particularly in their first few weeks. They have to learn to fend for themselves almost immediately as they are abandoned by their parents after only 10-12 days which is twice as quickly as Blackbirds, for example. However as Starlings are hole nesters far more of their nestlings fledge successfully than those of open nesting birds as fewer are lost to predators, so the net productivity is more or less the same.

Starlings were kept in cages as mimics and songbirds in former times and it is said that the theme of Mozart's piano concerto in G major is based on a tune whistled by his pet Starling. They were apparently regarded as sacred by Druids, possibly because they nested on Stonehenge! One of the most regrettable and economically damaging deliberate introductions of an alien species was that of the Starling to the USA. Within eighty years of a few birds being released in New York it had become one of the most abundant birds in North America, a considerable agricultural pest and competitor to native bird species. It is still increasing in some areas!

Starlings use a variety of nest sites including lofts, sheds and holes in walls but this very young bird was even more versatile, adopting the hair of its rescuer as a temporary home. In general, when rescuing cat victims or nestlings it is best to minimise contact with them to avoid imprinting, but they may well have other ideas!

MEDIUM BTO ALERT Has declined by more than a third in woodland habitats. Loss of traditional pastures may be a cause.

Male head distinctive, crown and nape are grey, only sides of head are brown. Warm browns streaked with black on back like the slightly smaller Tree Sparrow but with fewer white wing feather tips, only incomplete white collar, no black smudge on cheek and black bib larger.

Many gardeners are concerned about disappearing House Sparrows yet this species is still officially listed as a pest which can be destroyed at any time of year, so it is particularly vital that its numbers are monitored. Even the history of House Sparrow research illustrates the lowly regard in which this bird has been held. For many years it has been considered as literally a disposable bird, over-abundant and of no consequence, by almost everyone including biologists. As a result the poor old House Sparrow has been the subject of many destructive experiments that have given us much of our fundamental knowledge of bird's diet, anatomy and behaviour and how they change with the seasons. In 1940 an American

analysis of the contents of 8,004 dissected stomachs was published, with 838 different types of food identified. In other words, House Sparrows eat pretty much anything!

Not to be outdone, a German team ringed over five thousand young sparrows in the early fifties to investigate their movements. A good recovery rate was ensured by putting out poison in winter! This study showed that European House Sparrows don't really move very far at all. It is unlikely that a biologist today would dissolve five hundred sparrows in solvents to determine their body fat

When House Sparrows sit chirping in hedges it's hard to get a good view, but the males' grey crowns should be visible.

percentages, but this has also been done! Nowadays ornithologists use non-invasive methods such as ultrasound and better visual examination techniques but if we have confidence in these methods it is partly because their results match those of the pioneer 'bucket biologists', just as we owe much of our understanding of bird identification and structure to the 'shotgun ornithologists' of many years ago from

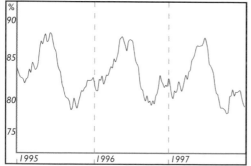

whom we inherit our reference collections of skins and eggs.

The sacrifice of so many birds also means that now the species seems less abundant in some areas we do at least have a fairly detailed knowledge of its biology, from which we can try to explain and hopefully mitigate any serious decline. The problem is that most of this previous research was carried out from the point of view of eliminating an abundant pest, rather than conserving a declining species.

House Sparrow garden records peak in the breeding season when the birds disperse to seek out nesting holes in all kinds of buildings. Autumn and winter flocks still generally prefer farmland.

House Sparrow *Passer domesticus*

Females different, generally lighter sandy browns streaked grey on wings. Creamy patch over eye. No bold black and white pattern on wing unlike female Chaffinch. No white moustache and bright white underparts unlike female Reed Bunting. Juveniles like brighter females.

61

Versatile feeders though they are, grain is by far the preferred food of House Sparrows all year round and this illuminates two of the many extraordinary aspects of this bird's biology, its worldwide distribution and strong association with human habitation. Africa is one of the few regions in which introduced House Sparrows have not been very successful, almost certainly due to competition from closely-related native sparrows. These may in fact be descendents of the ancestral House Sparrows which spread down the Nile valley into the near east at the time when grain cultivation was being developed. Subsequently the bird has followed farming throughout Europe and southern Asia.

Since 1800 the House Sparrow has spread through Siberia and the Americas as they were developed and is now possibly the most abundant bird species in the world, but almost everywhere relying on humans, their cultivated grain and particularly their buildings for nesting. This does suggest that changes in rural management could be causing problems for House Sparrows. The switch from spring to autumn-sown cereals means winter stubble fields are no longer available for the large flocks that used to gather there, and modern grain storage and handling systems are now sealed against birds with much less spillage. In addition the renovation or replacement of farm buildings and the refurbishment of suburban houses may well be reducing the supply of nest sites.

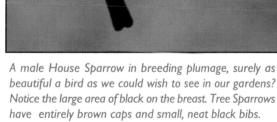

A male House Sparrow in breeding plumage, surely as beautiful a bird as we could wish to see in our gardens? Notice the large area of black on the breast. Tree Sparrows have entirely brown caps and small, neat black bibs.

One of the many intriguing aspects of House Sparrow behaviour is their short 'working day' in winter. While tits and finches feed frantically as nightfall approaches, sparrows can apparently afford to spend winter afternoons sitting in bushes cheeping at each other! Perhaps the very high energy content of cereal grain means they need relatively little time to consume enough food to last them the next 24 hours. Another suggestion is that they are very efficient feeders. Co-operating together in a sociable, cheeky gang that can dominate most feeding stations means they are wasting little energy in competition either with each other or with other birds. The obvious question then is, if they are so clever, why are they disappearing from so many areas?

Garden records provide supporting evidence of serious decline, more than 60% reduction in a small sample of rural populations since 1971.

From House Sparrow by white collar, black cheek smudge, smaller, slightly different call. Both sexes have biscuity brown crown ('gingernut') small black mask and bib, white feather tips in warm brown streaky wings. Well-groomed, cautious. Juveniles like washed-out adults.

120,000 pairs. Population has crashed since late 1970s especially in farmland. Range has contracted.

HIGH BTO ALERT

When designing a scientific population survey it can be difficult to decide which species should be included, especially similar-looking species which might be recorded inaccurately. Tree Sparrows are easy to separate from House Sparrows once observers have 'got their eye in' but this can take more time and practice than experienced sparrow spotters realise. By using a very large sample of gardens and recruiting volunteers with a spread of experience from beginner to expert, we hope that variations in accuracy will average out over time. Even if the absolute numbers of birds reported are slightly out we will still be able to monitor changes and trends effectively.

Brown crown should be obvious in both sexes, which cannot be told apart at all by their plumage.

Extracting trends from other volunteer surveys shows that recently this bird has declined seriously and is now of great concern in Britain although it does seem to be holding its own in Ireland. Little is known about the causes of this decline. Considerable research has been done on Tree Sparrows in other countries but almost all concerned with the impact of the birds on agriculture rather than their conservation. In most of China House Sparrows are absent and the Tree Sparrow is the common town and farm sparrow, considered such a pest that a campaign of eradication was ordered by Chairman Mao. Millions were killed but the rice harvest was apparently worse the following year. As Tree Sparrows feed their nestlings on insects this is not surprising.

For the rest of the year they largely depend on seeds, preferring smaller weed seeds to cereal grain. Modern herbicides and disappearing stubble fields mean that these are much harder to find as the seed bank in the soil of arable fields progressively declines. Studying Tree Sparrow breeding biology is made easier by their use of nest boxes although care is needed as they will desert their nests if disturbed at the wrong time. Interesting work in Poland found that some egg failures and nestling deaths were caused by bacterial infections, helping us to understand the problems of hole-nesting birds better and suggesting why Tree Sparrows regularly abandon productive nesting sites for no obvious reason.

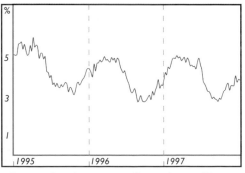
Seasonal cycle is generally similar to House Sparrow although reporting rate is much lower.

Tree Sparrow *Passer montanus*

Both sexes black and white wings, olive green rump. Male pinky-red face and breast, steel blue crown and nape. Female light brown, plainer, greyer than sandy female House Sparrow, Juveniles like females. Ground feeder, quite 'relaxed'. Loud musical song ends in flourish.

63

Wen seed-eating birds are gathered round a feeder in hard weather they may all seem to be exploiting the same food in the same way. In fact their natural dietary preferences differ according to the ecological niche occupied by each species and finches are a good example of how different species competing for food in the same habitat parcel out the available resources. All finches and buntings have stout bills for opening seeds but buntings mostly crush the seeds of cereals and grasses to extract the kernels. Finches prefer the seeds of 'dicotyledons', plants such as sunflowers which produce two 'seed leaves' unlike the single leaf produced by a germinating grass seed. They adroitly slice the larger husks open using the sharp edges of their lower mandible.

The Chaffinch and the closely-related Brambling are in a different genus from typical finches like the Greenfinch. Their behaviour is subtly different. They spend more time on the ground, picking up seeds and the small invertebrates which form the sole diet of their nestlings. Typical finches wean their nestlings onto seeds quite quickly, and the Yellowhammer (a bunting) brings half-ripe, milky cereal grains to its chicks just days after hatching.

A breeding male is fairly easy to identify, so when you see one observe the black and white markings on its wings. The less colourful females and juveniles have the same pattern.

Chaffinches and Bramblings do not use their feet to hold food, like tits. They do not cling to vegetation or hanging feeders as enthusiastically as typical finches such as the Goldfinch which also continuously twitter to each other whereas feeding Chaffinches are relatively quiet. In spring the males produce a loud, clear song but this is organised into short, distinct phrases.

Even within the same species, when resources are scarce birds behave differently. Most of our resident Chaffinches move very little but Scandinavian birds migrate, many wintering in southern Britain and Ireland. 'Differential wintering' in Chaffinches had been recognised by the 18th century when Linnaeus named the species *coelebs*, Latin for 'unmarried'. Most of the Chaffinches that stay in Scandinavia for the winter are males. Females migrate the furthest and hence predominate in Ireland during the coldest months.

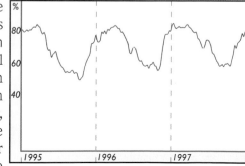

Seed-eating Chaffinches arrive for Christmas but peak in early spring when natural food is short.

In contrast with some other seed eaters, Chaffinches have increased by as much as a quarter in the last 20 years. **7,500,000 pairs.**

Bright white rump, carroty orange shoulders and breast, white belly. Winter visitor only. Male head darkens as winter progresses. Beautiful scalloping on mantle. Head can seem stripey. Less white on wing than Chaffinch. Quite nervous ground feeder, often in small flock.

50,000 — 2,000,000 winter visitors. Less than ten pairs breed, may be colonising slowly. 'Amber listed' due to low breeding numbers.

The winter of 1997/98 showed that relationships between bird behaviour and weather are not always obvious. Winter does not have to be particularly cold to force Bramblings into gardens. Whenever beech mast runs low in the woods these interesting migrants may visit our feeding stations. Check any flock of winter finches for bright white rumps! Often one or two juveniles or females arrive first as differential wintering applies to this species and the dominant males tend to fly the least distance from their breeding areas. These early arrivals can appear rather like Chaffinches but their heads seem bigger and flight bouncier. There is much less white on the wing and the white rump is usually obvious. The back of the head can look more stripey than field guide pictures indicate but there will always be a hint of carrot on the 'shoulders' and the top of the breast.

Males may arrive later in the winter, they always show more orange than females but only in April do they start to show the black heads of their breeding plumage. Bramblings are generally independent of humans and live a wild life in mature forests, ideally with clearings. Even in winter they rarely use agricultural resources, preferring beech mast which they feed on in flocks that are sometimes huge. Winter roosts in central Europe may contain

Bramblings arrive in our gardens in winter plumage. Grey feather tips will wear off this male's head to reveal deep black, but by then he will be on his way home. Check for white rump and orange on breast.

millions of birds and sometimes stop traffic when they descend to glean food from the sides of a road. Their movements were studied by Swiss ornithologist Lukas Jenni who showed that Bramblings migrate the shortest distance they can, stopping as soon as they find beech mast. However snow prevents them from feeding and forces them to move further as winter progresses.

Nesting in large forests, they are not short of sites and hence their breeding behaviour differs from the Chaffinch which has to nest in a more competitive environment. Male Chaffinches aggressively defend nest sites from rivals, but Bramblings only defend their mates, often nesting together in loose colonies.

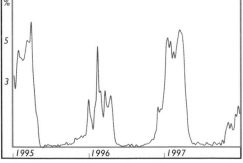

So far very few gardens have reported Bramblings but this could change if food is short.

Brambling *Fringilla montifringilla*

Male green, wings and tail flash yellow. Female browner, dull, less yellow. Juvenile streaky, looks very brown, less black and yellow in wing than young Goldfinch. Stocky, stout bill. Yellowy-green rump. More 'sober' than smaller, acrobatic Siskin. Monotonous burbling song.

I n southern and eastern England Greenfinches are becoming permanent fixtures in many gardens, especially since smaller, softer black sunflower seeds have become widely available. Fixture seems the right word sometimes as they apparently attach themselves to a seed feeder for hours on end, placidly munching away and showing very little competitive or territorial behaviour by bird standards. In fact Greenfinches only defend a very small area around their nests. Otherwise they seem calm in each other's company, much more upright and sober citizens than busy little Siskins that hang upside down, churring at each other.

Although this species seems to be with us all year round, in fact the birds in the garden in winter may not be the same as those in summer as many Greenfinches do migrate, albeit not very far. Garden ringing has suggested that English birds head generally south-west in the winter, and how far they move probably depends on how cold the weather is. Some Norwegian birds visit our east coast in most winters. The further west and north your garden, the more unusual will be a Greenfinch, they are virtually absent from the north-west corner of Scotland and Ireland. They seem to need a lowland 'edge' habitat, with tall leafy trees bordering a good supply of seeds.

A Greenfinch firmly attached to a seed feeder! They will appreciate seeds all year round if provided.

Traditional mixed farming with pollarded oaks, copses, winter stubbles and unimproved pasture full of invertebrates would have been ideal for Greenfinches and so many other typical garden birds. Modern intensive farming makes life harder for them, particularly the destruction or flailing of hedges as Greenfinches relied on a good variety of tough seeds remaining on wild shrubs in late winter, to enter the breeding season in good condition. They are particularly partial to wild rose hips, their powerful beaks enabling them to tackle a wider range of seeds than other finches. If a continuous supply of black sunflower seeds is available in a garden, they breed early and manage several broods, bringing streaky brown fledglings to feeders as late as November.

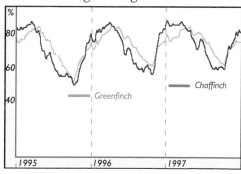

Seasonal cycle for Greenfinch is similar to Chaffinch but intriguingly, the timing is offset

MEDIUM BTO ALERT Population stable but nest records show a worrying increase in nest failures. 700,000 pairs.

Carduelis chloris **Greenfinch**

66

The only small finch which has red, white and black on head and bright golden yellow contrasting with black on wings. Blue Tit size but somehow looks a bit bigger with its bold colouring and personality. Agile, bounces around in small flocks, clear call, twittering song.

'Amber listed' due to serious population decline in the late 1980s However numbers now seem to have recovered.

The exotic appearance and great charm of the Goldfinch were its undoing in the last century when huge numbers were trapped for the cagebird trade. Enthusiasts taught them to do tricks for visitors including pulling tiny carts and drawing up miniature buckets of water from 'wells' and in fact one of this bird's many traditional names is 'Draw-water'. Other less obvious nicknames include 'King Harry', perhaps from the red face? The wild population was somewhat depleted by the demand for pets but recovered when the sale of wild-caught birds was finally banned. Unfortunately this bird's favoured habitat of scrubby 'waste ground' with plenty of tall seeding weeds is now threatened by development and 'tidying' around towns and by the sanitisation of farmland with selective herbicides. However one trend in land management which helps Goldfinches is that for wildlife gardening, especially the increasing acceptance of self-sown biennial 'weeds' such as teasels among decorative plantings.

Teasel heads will stand outdoors through winter and can be refilled with small seeds.

Teasel seeds are quite easy to come by and even potted plants are available from some garden centres but do remember it is illegal to uproot plants from the wild. If their seed heads are left to stand through the winter roving flocks of Goldfinches should spot them pretty quickly and nip down to investigate although the visitors may not be noticed immediately as these birds can be qute unobtrusive around a garden despite their bright colouring. Often their twittering calls are heard before they are actually spotted among the plants, until they get used to your garden when they seem to become more confident. One way to keep them coming is to refill the teasel heads with small seed. Niger seed is ideal, chicory seed also works although it does germinate

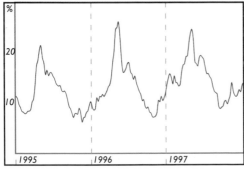

One of the most extraordinary Garden BirdWatch reporting rate plots, with a distinct and regular peak at the end of every April.

and take over the garden rather readily. Other seed heads favoured by Goldfinches in a fashionably untidy garden include lavender, cosmos and of course large seeding thistles although these really do spread! When the birds have been successfully attracted, they quickly learn to use black sunflower seed feeders. These are the easiest way to feed Goldfinches all year, once they get the hang of them.

In autumn quite large flocks may gather, some gardeners with larger

Goldfinch *Carduelis carduelis*

Juveniles can be tricky as they have no red, white or black on their dull brown heads but the vivid gold and black pattern on the wings is already present, showing more yellow and black in wing than juvenile Greenfinch which has more greenish tone overall and is a bit bigger.

67

plots reporting nearly two hundred birds at a time. If the weather gets cold, most Goldfinches migrate in a south-westerly direction, pausing wherever they find food and crossing the Channel if necessary. The sharp annual peak in the Garden BirdWatch reporting rate plot probably these migrants returning to breed at the end of April but finding very little more natural food available than there was when they departed. Garden feeders offer a useful standby at this difficult time. Behavioural studies confirm that the start of the breeding season when food is short is really the only time when pairs of Goldfinches aggressively defend food from other Goldfinches. By contrast, in autumn and winter their feeding flocks are sociable and well-organised, with constant communication. Individual birds joining flocks benefit from shared information about food and improved vigilance.

If supplementary food is offered in the breeding season they will take advantage and in fact there will may well be several different pairs visiting at different times of day. Goldfinches are sociable birds even when they pair off to breed and

there will probably be a small 'neighbourhood' of nests in the area. To other birds they are less sociable, in fact quite quarrelsome, shooing other species off bird tables even when there is plenty of food. With their great agility and finely pointed bills they specialise in extracting small seeds from tall plants which no other finch in the British Isles can deal with. Monopolising this resource means they are probably not used to dining in company.

To the casual observer Goldfinches all look alike but with a close view of the face they can in fact be sexed quite accurately. If the red extends behind the eye and the bristles around the base of the bill are black, rather than grey, the bird is a male.

The nesting behaviour of the Goldfinch was recorded in detail by Peter Conder in a pioneering study, particularly extraordinary because it was performed while he was a prisoner of war in 1943. Conder and fellow-prisoners spent nine hours a day watching three Goldfinch nests and their meticulous records were published after the war as a scientific paper in the prestigious British Ornithologists Union journal, *Ibis*. This paper ends with a wistful note that 22 days after hatching, the Goldfinch families left the camp, unlike the ornithologists! However, like our many housebound Garden BirdWatch volunteers, they found that even in unlikely locations there is always another fascinating aspect of bird life to watch and study.

Finch breeding populations are hard to estimate as they forage around a wide area and mnay nests in gardens are not counted. 275,000 pairs.

Recording Siskins as they feed in our gardens will contribute to monitoring a fascinating change in the breeding range of this species. Traditionally considered a winter visitor, Siskins are now staying here all year in ever-increasing numbers and some of the birds on your feeders in cold weather may now be British-bred. Ringing recoveries show that quite a few Siskins wintering in Norfolk, for example, are actually Scottish birds. Gardens near conifer plantations are the most likely to have Siskins on the feeders all year round including the delightful youngsters and as more pinewoods mature and their invertebrate communities develop, hopefully more of these interesting finches will breed successfully.

Females lack the males black crown and bright greens but are still much more contrasty than a Greenfinch with light belly and black and yellow wing pattern.

One of the obvious features which distinguishes Siskins from Greenfinches, apart from smaller size, black on the wings, distinctive calls and more acrobatic behaviour, is the very pointed bill. Like Goldcrests and Coal Tits, these birds are adapted to feeding in conifers which means extracting tiny food items from tight spaces, although as finches are mostly vegetarian outside the breeding season adult Siskins take mainly seeds from the cones rather than small insects. The banks of rivers and streams within woods are a favourite habitat both for breeding, when invertebrates to feed the chicks are often gathered along the water's edge, and for gathering in flocks to feed on alder cones in winter. Some gardeners claim that red peanut bags have attracted Siskins to feeding stations because they remind the birds of giant alder cones.

If Siskins are setting up home in your area you may be lucky enough to see the display flight of the males in which they ascend, loop and circle repeatedly above their proposed nest site, singing all the while. These so-called 'song flights' are performed by quite a few bird species to attract the attention of potential mates but the tiny Siskin's

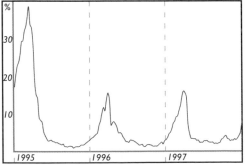

Traditionally winter only, but changing slowly.

Siskin *Carduelis spinus*

From Greenfinch by smaller size, black on wings, darker male's head, sharper pointed bill, brighter belly, more acrobatic, readily feeding upside down. Greenfinch has yellow stripe down folded wing, Siskin has yellow stripe across folded wing. Distinctive twittering song and calls.

69

display is a particularly strong effort and may even be performed by several males at once. Once heard well, their song is easily recognised and when given more or less continuously by a flock gathered around the garden in early spring, it can be an amazing 'wall of sound' experience upon walking out of one's front door first thing in the morning. It is thin and high but has a peculiar yodelling quality with a characteristic 'dluee' note and often a strange wheezey 'suck note' at the ends of phrases. In a letter, one Garden BirdWatcher transcribed a Siskin's call as 'doodly doodly sheeeeep'! Like all the *Carduelis* finches these are very vocal birds, seemingly in constant communication with each other.

Siskins can seem rather pugnacious and argumentative but in fact among themselves they are sociable birds, often nesting close together in colonies of half a dozen pairs or more. The males sometimes fly about in small groups, visiting their females in turn and can often be seen feeding each other as well as offering food to the females during courtship. Spanish ornithologist Juan Carlos Senar studied a captive group of Siskins and showed that between males, food was always passed from a subordinate bird to a dominant. At the start of the breeding season the males often started fights, which rarely led to any injury but instead petered out into ritualised mutual feeding movements as the winner became clear. Subsequently the dominant bird regularly demanded food from the loser, taking it gently from the subordinate bird's beak. Only males seem to do this, females are fed by courting males but never feed each other. It was very interesting to find this behaviour in a European finch because mutual feeding was previously associated only with very

social, colonial species like weavers and scrub jays. Senar interpreted this observation as an integrating behaviour that reduces aggression in the breeding season when time and energy wasted on disputes could be better used.

Once the eggs have hatched, males are too busy provisioning broods to bother about feeding each other so the peak time for this fascinating behaviour is early spring, when you might well notice it taking place around your own peanut feeders.

Like Great Spotted Woodpeckers, Siskins have discovered that peanuts are just as good as tree seeds, their favourite winter food. Many people claim to have first attracted them with red bags, but in fact they will use any kind of peanut feeder.

The breeding population is not well-monitored because very few volunteers census birds in our northern and western conifer forests.

Carduelis spinus **Siskin**

White rump, black cap. Male breast, belly bright red, mantle grey. Female breast, belly, mantle brown, both black and white wings, white vent, black tail tip. Juvenile like female without black cap. Quiet, shy, 'chunky' sparrow size, thick bill, nibbles buds, shells seeds clumsily.

300,000 pairs. Hard to monitor. Declined sharply in the late 1970s and may now be dropping again. **HIGH BTO ALERT**

The Bullfinch is a rather enigmatic bird, spending much of its time deep in deciduous woods and thickets, easily overlooked despite the bright colours of the male. Nor does it sing loudly like other finches. A soft, low whistling call keeps family groups together as they forage inconspicuously among the branches, only their white rumps really giving them away. Neither intensive farming nor conifer plantations are good for this species and strategies such as setaside or the planting of game cover crops which can help other farmland seed-eaters cannot compensate for the fragmentation or loss of mature mixed woods. Still persecuted in some fruit growing areas for eating tree buds, Bullfinches have declined by more than half. Numbers may be falling again after a period of stability.

Female Bullfinches lack the bright red of males but still have a clear white rump and obvious black cap. Juveniles look like females but without black caps.

Recently Bullfinches have started to use seed feeders, probably through shortage of food in the countryside as well as the provision of more suitable foods by gardeners. Softer black sunflower seeds are closer to natural foods than the very dry striped varieties. If a feeder is placed near a bush so the birds can quickly retreat when disturbed they may become regular visitors. Often the male sits on the feeder while the female gleans below. The seeds of Honesty are another favourite food, rather annoyingly for flower arrangers!

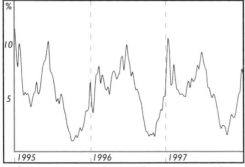

Reporting rate peaks in midsummer as nestlings demand more food, and some Bullfinches also visit in cold winters. They virtually disappear from gardens in autumn when tree seeds are plentiful.

In late winter when seeds run low, Bullfinches eat young tree buds, which does not endear them to fruit growers. The buds of cultivated trees swell earlier than native species providing a more nutritious meal at a time of food shortage. Ash keys are a favourite winter food but the seeds produced by this tree vary greatly in quantity from year to year. When the ash crop is poor, Bullfinches turn to tree buds earlier but even then most trees produce a large surplus of buds and some fruits are left for us.

Bullfinch   Pyrrhula pyrrhula

Yellow, no bold black and white. Chestnut brown rump. Male glows bright yellow, female duller, juvenile streaky. Sparrow size, looks slimmer. Quite long, dark, flicking tail has thin white edges, notched end. Neat, triangular silver-grey bill. Sociable ground feeder in winter.

71

Very much a rural bird of arable farms and traditional hedgerows, Yellowhammers may be forced to overcome their reluctance to use garden feeders if the countryside continues to change. Organochlorine seed dressings killed many of them in the 1950s and they have recently started to decline again. In particular the wholesale switch from spring-sown to autumn-sown cereals must surely affect a species which feeds largely on grain and larger grass seeds and was very much associated with the winter stubble fields which have all but disappeared from modern farming systems.

An apparent need to maintain quite long breeding territories along established hedgerows rather than defend small patches of land like other birds could be a factor that prevents them from moving into suburbia and they do not compete particularly well with more aggressive species. However on mixed farms Yellowhammers cheerfully scrounge grain from around animal feeding troughs and chicken runs so artificial structures do not particularly intimidate them. In gardens they will appreciate food provided on the ground, preferably near to cover.

Females are quite yellow on the head but drab compared to breeding males which can look almost 'day-glo' in spring. Try to see the chestnut rump.

Grain is preferred, it may need protecting from pigeons with some kind of cage. Sunflower hearts, which do not require removal from a husk, are also ideal.

Dr Antonios Kyrkos studied Yellowhammers intensively for several years and learnt a lot about the problems faced by our farmland birds. Yellowhammers depend on cultivated cereals for winter survival, especially now that traditional hay meadows have been replaced by silage grasses which are cut before they seed. Food shortages in winter and early spring are almost certainly affecting breeding performance. Yellowhammers on organic farms still produce enough young to maintain their populations but birds on intensive farms were found to be declining and likely to disappear.

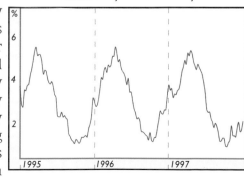

Even at such a low reporting rate we see a clear seasonal cycle, suggesting that spring is a time of serious food shortage for breeding birds.

Emberiza citrinella **Yellowhammer**

White 'moustache'. Male head dark, black in spring, white collar. Female and juvenile sparrow-like but white edges to notched tail, light belly, streaky browns on back are brighter, more rufous than duller, sandy female House Sparrow, flicks tail more, call quite different.

350,000 pairs. Population decline of more than 50% since the late 1970s seems to be continuing.

HIGH BTO ALERT

Reed Buntings visit very few gardens but are gradually using more feeding stations, especially now that smaller, softer sunflower seeds which more closely resemble their natural food are widely available. Any change in their use of gardens over the next few years may reflect a continuing decline and indicate how they are having to adapt their behaviour in response to habitat loss. Reed Buntings are associated with dense, tall vegetation and shrubs on moist soil in lowland areas, often bordering reedy dykes or marshes in which they can forage for seeds and invertebrates with

little competition from less agile birds such as sparrows and finches which tend to exclude them from more accessible resources.

Wet reedbeds are of little use for breeding as Reed Buntings prefer to nest on the ground. This again shows how important mixed habitats with edges, slight level changes and transitions between vegetation types are for our traditional farmland birds and how easy it might be to inadvertantly remove a vital component of a bird's seasonal cycle by tidying and

Look out for Reed Buntings among ground feeding birds in hard weather. Sunflower hearts are ideal.

'improving' the countryside.

BTO ecologist Dr Niall Burton studied Reed Buntings in oilseed rape fields which can provide quite good foraging and nesting opportunities. Rape fields are either cut or sprayed with herbicide early in summer to kill and dry the plants before harvest. Second broods of Reed Bunting nestlings were destroyed by mechanical cutting but survived herbicide spraying, which gave them an extra two weeks to fledge and therefore increased annual nesting success. So where birds have adapted to intensive farming, chemical

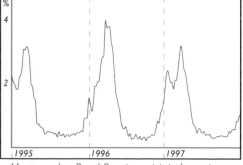

Most garden Reed Buntings visit in late winter.

sprays are not always necessarily the worst management option.

Reed Buntings were one of the first birds to have their relationships studied by DNA analysis. Only half the nestlings were the offspring of the pair in whose nest they were reared! The breeding behaviour of apparently monogamous birds has since been found to be much more complex than previously realised.

Reed Bunting *Emberiza schoeniclus*

Some frequent garden visitors are not included in Garden BirdWatch because it is difficult either to identify them or to decide if they are really making use of the garden. These include Chiffchaff and Willow Warbler, Swift and Swallow. Other birds readily use gardens but are scarce or hard to observe. It's well worth keeping an eye open for rarities, especially if your garden is on the coast or provides 'oasis' facilities such as a pond in a dry area. Grey Herons are the best known large garden predators but often visit before dawn while we are still asleep. In areas where they have been reintroduced, Red Kites can be attracted even to fairly small gardens. Squashed rabbits collected off the road work well! In a hard winter, Waxwings are just as likely to be seen in gardens as anywhere else and in parts of Scotland the rare Crested Tit will take peanuts just as gratefully as a Blue Tit. Crossbills sneak down to garden ponds and the extraordinary Wryneck visits suburban lawns, pausing for a meal of ants while on migration. Also recorded from time to time during freak weather conditions are 'accidentals' — species such as waders or auks that would normally never use a garden. Escaped cagebirds are troublesome to identify as there is such a vast range of species kept. Canaries and Zebra Finches often turn up in gardens.

Ring-necked Parakeets are a worrying addition to some garden bird lists.

Although fascinating, records of very rare birds may not be of great value in monitoring bird populations. The unusual garden birds of greatest conservation concern are declining native species which might benefit from feeding, introduced species and birds changing their distributions. Linnet and Corn Bunting visit rural plots, both have 'High BTO Alerts' issued due to serious declines, as does the Redpoll which has started to use feeders in some areas. The 'red' listed Cirl Bunting is still occasionally a garden bird in the south-west and if anyone is feeding Turtle Doves in their garden, we would love to know! The most worrying introduced bird seen in gardens is probably the Ring-necked Parakeet which is a serious agricultural pest in parts of its natural range.

Of great interest are birds expanding or contracting their ranges, possibly due to climate change. The Serin is a tiny finch common in continental gardens and now well worth looking out for in southern England. Exotic continentals such as the Hoopoe may not be far behind if global warming continues. This of course could be very bad news for migrants such as warblers and flycatchers if their winter habitats deteriorate and the arrival of new competitors might also affect our native residents, so it's very important and interesting to monitor these long-term changes.

To monitor populations, shouldn't we count the exact numbers of birds?

The aim is not to calculate the exact population figures to but detect **changes** in the way birds are using gardens. If we collect simple data consistently and compare results from year to year, important changes will show up. With enough data, we can work out whether these are happening everywhere or in a particular area so it's important to keep the survey simple, enabling busy people to take part. To detect change, we need a little data from many gardens over a wide area, rather than detailed records from a few.

It is not yet clear how bird numbers reported in gardens relate to their absolute populations, this may vary from species to species. One of Garden

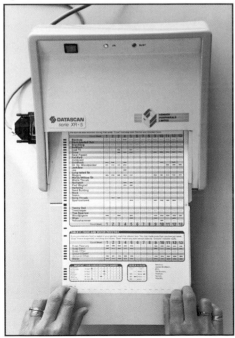

The scanner needs flat, clean forms.

BirdWatch's important contributions will be to better understanding of these relationships, by comparing any changes with data from other habitats.

How were the survey species chosen?

From our previous, small scale garden surveys, we found which birds visited gardens often enough to be practically monitored during survey participants' normal domestic activities, rather than requiring intensive birdwatching effort. Again, the aim is to keep it simple to enable maximum participation.

What happens to our count forms?

They are fed through an 'optical mark recognition' scanning machine and this converts the small 'blobs' into electronic data. This is fed directly into the BTO's computer data archive system and is immediately available for processing and analysis. It takes several days to scan all the forms but this is still far more efficient than typing in your garden bird records by hand. However it does mean that the forms must be returned to us clean and flat, with no marks at all other than 'blobs' in the little boxes. Any kind of writing or marks on the forms cause them to be rejected by the scanner, unless it is within the 'name and address' box which the machine is programmed to ignore. The best way to return forms is to fold them carefully in half along the line marked 'fold here' and post them in a C5 (229 x 162 mm) envelope. A piece of thin card such as cereal packet is not essential but helps to keep them flat in the post.

Is expensive bird food worth the money?
Birds feed wherever they can safely find the most nutritious, appropriate, and convenient food at any particular time of year. In a hard winter even the cheapest grain or bread may their best option but as soon as they can find anything better, they will go elsewhere.

However, nutritious near-natural foods such as black sunflower seeds may be the best food available anywhere all year for some birds, especially finches. In winter they also help species which cannot eat cereal or scraps. So better foods increase the range of species helped and help them for more of the year. Also, fresh seeds are more nutritious than stale ones. Cheap mixes may contain last year's seed so may nourish fewer birds per pound spent than better quality, fresh supplies.

This baby Robin was one of four hauled out of a nestbox and dumped on the patio by a cat. Try not to make birds more vulnerable.

Mouldy peanuts actually poison birds. Birdfood Standards Association members guarantee their peanuts are tested so it's worth looking for their logo.

Does feeding birds endanger them at all?
Try not to make birds more vulnerable to cats. If necessary place feeders right inside a hedge or suspend them high off the ground using a pole or from a first floor window. Don't let droppings or food waste accumulate, infections are easily spread to other birds, pets and even children. Keep feeders reasonably clean and move them from time to time. If large numbers of ground-feeding birds appear, reduce the food. Avoid cereal if it attracts many pigeons.

What about 'wildlife gardening'?
Even birds which eat seeds as adults depend on invertebrates to feed their nestlings, so they cannot breed in a sterile garden no matter how many seed feeders are provided. Most insects need particular food plants, exotic plants support only generalists like slugs and aphids. Plant native plants!

Fruiting shrubs and small trees are especially valuable as they offer nesting cover and berries. Look in local hedgerows as the plants do vary somewhat with locality, but you can't go far wrong with Hawthorn *Craetagus spp.*, Elder *Sambucus nigra* or Hazel *Corylus avellana*. Others to try include wild Privet *Ligustrum vulgare*, Blackthorn *Prunus spinosa*, Spindle *Euonymus europaeus*, Rowan *Sorbus aucuparia* and Whitebeam *Sorbus aria* as well as Holly and Yew (female plants for berries!) And don't forget apple and pear trees provide plentiful food if left unsprayed, as do climbers like Ivy.

Try to cut out insecticides, relying on natural predators to keep pests under control. Things will get worse before they get better but after a couple of years a small hand sprayer with liquid derris for emergencies should be all you need.

Books:
Ideal for beginners:
Attracting Birds to your Garden
Stephen Moss & David Cottridge
New Holland. ISBN 185368 569 0 (hbk)
Comprehensive guide to bird gardening and identification, fully illustrated with superb colour photographs.

The Complete Garden Bird Book
Mark Golley, Stephen Moss & David Daly
New Holland ISBN 1 85368 581 X (pbk)
Smaller and a bit cheaper, identifies all common garden birds with particularly clear colour paintings.

Field Guides:
Pocket Guide to the Birds of Britain & North-West Europe.
Chris Kightley, Steve Madge & Dave Nurney.
Pica Press. ISBN 1 873403 49 6 (pbk)
Handy size to carry, comprehensive and clear.

The Shell Easy Bird Guide
Rob Hume & Peter Hayman
Macmillan, ISBN 0 333 65420 X (pbk)
Ideal for younger birders with both colour photos and paintings for every species. A bit heavier to carry.

Birds of Europe
Lars Jonsson
Christopher Helm, ISBN 0 7136 4422 2 (pbk)
For serious birders travelling anywhere in Europe

Practical Handbooks:
Nestboxes. Chris du Feu
BTO Guide 23. ISBN 0 903793 29 6 (pbk)
Standard reference book for nestbox constructors.

Songs and Calls:
Garden Bird Sounds Compact Disc
Wildsounds. ISBN 1 898665 76 1 (CD) Songs and calls of 70 species, each announced to aid learning.

All of the above should be available from BTO sales. Telephone 01842 750050 for prices and availability.

Organic and Wildlife Gardening:
A good selection of books, as well as seeds and equipment, are available from *The Organic Gardening Catalogue*. Telephone 01932 253666 for a free copy.

Binoculars:
Many birders prefer European binoculars such as Leica or Swarovski but there are plenty of excellent cheaper models ideal for garden use. However this sector of the market does change rapidly. Decide a budget, buy a magazine such as *Birdwatching*, compare prices advertised by specialist suppliers. Then visit one of their shops or an event such as the British BirdWatching Fair at Rutland Water to try your shortlisted models. Check compatibility with spectacles, comfort, weight and **minimum focus distance**. Not all cheap binoculars can focus on the bird table from your seat by a window. 8x42 is a good general-purpose size, the first number is the magnification, the second the diameter of the lens through which light enters, bigger means brighter, smaller means lighter (weight!) Try and support a supplier belonging to the BTO's *Birds and Business Alliance*. Old window panes may need replacing with modern glass before your binoculars will focus properly through them.

Bird Food and Feeders:
CJ Wildbird Foods Ltd.
Garden BirdWatch sponsors. Participants in the project receive their catalogue automatically. Others can telephone 01743 709545 for a free copy.

Local Projects and Activities:
Bird Clubs, Natural History Societies, RSPB local Member's Groups and Wildlife Trusts organise meetings, outings and conservation projects and new members are always welcome. Information on how to contact local groups (and much more) is compiled in the annual **Birdwatchers Yearbook** (ISBN 0 951 49659 X), obtainable by mail order from Buckingham Press, 25 Manor Park, Maids Moreton, MK18 1QX, telephone 01280 813931. Alternatively, enquire at a library or reserve visitor centre.

Resources

Monographs compile the available information about a species, usually with original research by the author. Ornithological monographs tend to be very readable and suitable for non-scientists. Books asterisked below are introductory level and suitable for beginners. Some of the books listed are out of print or even collector's items. However, they may be borrowed from the BTO lending library as a privilege of full BTO membership.

If you have enjoyed Garden BirdWatch or this booklet, please consider joining the BTO, as membership subscriptions underwrite much of our other work. Please call the membership unit, or write for more details.

Blackbird, Redwing, Song Thrush
British Thrushes by Eric Simms. Collins New Naturalist, 1978. ISBN 0 00 219670 0

Blackcap
The Blackcap by C.F.Mason. Hamlyn Species Guides, 1995, ISBN 0 600 58006 7

Crows, Rook, Jackdaw, Jay
The Crows by Franklin Coombs. Batsford, 1978. ISBN 0 7134 1327 1

Dunnock
Dunnock Behaviour and Social Evolution by N.B.Davies. Oxford, 1992. ISBN 0 19 854675 0

Fieldfare
The Fieldfare by David Norman. Hamlyn Species Guides, 1994, ISBN 0 600 57961 1

Magpie
The Magpies by T.R.Birkhead. T & AD Poyser, 1991. ISBN 0 85661 067 4

Nuthatch
The Nuthatches by Erik Matthysen. T & AD Poyser, 1998. ISBN 0 85661 101 8

Owls
Owls byChris Mead*.Whittet Books,1987. ISBN 0 905483 59 6

Robin
The Life of the Robin by David Lack, 1943
Robins by Chris Mead.*
Whittet Books, 1984, ISBN 0 905483 36 7
The Robin by M.Read, M. King & J. Allsop. *
Blandford,1992. ISBN 0 713721 56 1

Sparrows
Books by J.Denis Summers Smith:
The House Sparrow. Collins New Nat., 1963
The Sparrows. T & A.D.Poyser, 1988
ISBN 0 85661 048 8
In Search of Sparrows. * T & A.D.Poyser, 1992
ISBN 0 85661 073 9
The Tree Sparrow. Published by author, 1995.
ISBN 0 952 5383 0 X

Sparrowhawk
The Sparrowhawk by Ian Newton. T & AD Poyser, 1986. ISBN 0 85661 041 0

Starling
The Starling by Christopher Feare, Oxford University Press, 1984. ISBN 0 19 217705 2

Tits
British Tits by Christopher Perrins, Collins New Naturalist, 1979, ISBN 0 00 219537 2
The Great Tit by Andrew Gosler. Hamlyn Species Guides, 1993. ISBN 0 600 57950 6

Woodpigeon
The Wood-pigeon by R.K.Murton. Collins New Naturalist, 1965

Wren
The Wren by Edward A.Armstrong. Collins New Naturalist, 1955

The BTO members lending library is one of Britain's largest ornithological collections.

Contact the Membership Unit on 01842 750050 for details of how to become a full member of the BTO.

Ecology

The study of how animals and plants live togther and how they depend on one another and on their environment in 'ecosystems'. The planet Earth is one huge ecosystem but for practical study, ecologists subdivide it according to the questions to be answered. While one ecologist studies the ecosystem of a whole forest, another may study the ecosystem of a single tree, on which many creatures may depend. Others focus on areas such as populations and movements, communities and diversity, productivity, animal behaviour, fossil history and evolutionary relationships.

Ecological Niche

The particular resources within an ecosystem used by a particular species. The 'fundamental niche' of most garden birds is very wide as they are versatile and can exploit many different resources. However, competition tends to limit them to a rather narrower range of resources, known as their 'realised niche', which changes with the seasons.

Ecosystem

A naturally-occurring, self-sustaining, evolving system of organisms and their resources, with *communities* of living creatures, *flows and cycles* of energy and chemicals and *webs* of interdependence.

Ethology

The study of behaviour.

Granivores

Birds which eat almost entirely seeds may be described as granivorous, in contrast to insectivores which eat mostly insects. Strictly, most birds are more or less omnivores, eating a wide variety of different foods according to the season.

Invertebrates

Animals without backbones, including the main prey of most garden birds such as worms, molluscs, insects and their larvae. Small invertcbrates are essential food for the nestlings of all garden birds except pigeons. Their availability may determine breeding success of songbirds.

Passerines

Shorthand for *Passeriformes*, the largest taxonomic order of birds. *Passer* is Latin for sparrow and all members of this order, from Goldcrest to Raven, share the sparrow's basic anatomy. Also known as 'perching birds' or 'songbirds'. All Garden BirdWatch species are passerines except Sparrowhawk (*Accipitriformes*), Black-headed Gull (*Charadriiformes*), pigeons and doves (*Columbiformes*), Tawny Owl (*Strigiformes*) and Great Spotted Woodpecker (*Piciformes*).

Ornithology

The study of birds. From a Greek word *ornis* meaning bird. From the Latin for bird, *avis*, we get aviary and aviation but 'aviology' sounds rather awkward!

Polyandry

A mating system in which females mate with more than one male. Social polyandry, in which a female and more than one male forage together and breed cooperatively is unusual in birds, but Dunnocks are an example. On the other hand, opportunistic polyandry involving usually clandestine matings outside a socially monogamous pair bond, is extremely common in birds.

Polygyny
Males mating with more than one female, also common in birds.

Scientific Literature
Scientific results are published in journals and reports which are "refereed" i.e. examined and criticised by independent scientists before publication. The BTO journals *Bird Study* and *Ringing and Migration* enable amateur ornithologists to publish the results of their own projects alongside professionals, to the same high standard.

Statistics
Often used to mean collections of data from experiments, counts or surveys but more properly refers to the branch of mathematics concerned with organising, summarising and evaluating such data. Calculating an average is a very simple example of using a statistical technique.

Statistically Significant
If data from an experiment or survey seem to show a meaningful result, mathematical tests are applied to find the probability that this result just occurred by chance. In biology, if this probability is less than 5% the result is said to be statistically significant. When scientific results are formally published, details of these 'significance tests' are included. These techniques are especially important in ecological monitoring. For example, we could never count every single bird in all our gardens so changes occurring in the whole population can only be inferred from any changes we may have observed in the much smaller sample that we can practically monitor.

Systematic Order
The arrangement of records or descriptions of organisms in order of their evolutionary relationships rather than, for example, in alphabetic order of their 'common' English names. Most ornithologists use the order of species published by Professor Voous in 1977 which has stood the test of time although the latest taxonomic methods may yet come up with further modifications.

Taxonomy
The science of classifying and naming things. A group of related organisms such as an order, family or genus is called a taxon (plural taxa). Early taxonomists classified birds based on their plumage, anatomy and behaviour. Modern taxonomists study the evolutionary history of organisms using all the available evidence, including examining their genes for relationships using knowledge and techniques derived from so-called 'genetic engineering'.

Who says pigeons are no use to science? This may be a top ornithologist of the future!

* seasonal visitor, year-round average not meaningful

sizes are minimum box entrance hole diameters